For Michael & Tricia

with best wishes

David Steel

PLEASE WIPE YOUR
CRUTCH ON THE
TOWEL BEFORE
YOU LEAVE

PLEASE WIPE YOUR CRUTCH ON THE TOWEL BEFORE YOU LEAVE

David Strutt

The Book Guild Ltd
Sussex, England

First published in Great Britain in 2001 by
The Book Guild Ltd
25 High Street,
Lewes, East Sussex
BN7 2LU

Typesetting in Times by
Keyboard Services, Luton, Bedfordshire

Printed in Great Britain by
Bookcraft (Bath) Ltd, Avon

A catalogue record for this book is
available from the British Library

ISBN 1 85776 534 6

*Dedicated to the doctors and nurses
who took us to pieces and put us back
together again*

FOREWORD

It is almost exactly six months since I visited David and Alison, and sat on their terrace in the sun, drinking tea and catching up on the news of their traumatic year. Alison was very weary and drawn from the effects of her chemotherapy, and David, still leaning heavily on a stick, was walking with a marked limp. Oddly though, what I remember most was their wonderful ability to chuckle about everything which had befallen them. I had the feeling that their capacity to find humour along the rockiest of roads had brought them through. It was just like people say: laughter *is* the best medicine. When I heard that a book had emerged from their trials, I had no idea that it could possibly be a book like *this*! Just glimpsing the title had me in stitches.

When we discussed *Return To Me*, the film I had just finished, the story of Grace who had undergone a heart transplant, they asked me whether portraying a character coming to terms with disfigurement had been difficult. I told them that at times it had, and that it had caused me to reflect deeply on how we take our health and our well-being for granted. We never know when the tide of good fortune may turn, placing us, or our loved ones, at the mercy of physical difficulties beyond our understanding or control. At such times, as we are swept up in the pain, the worry, the distress and the disillusionment which inevitably attach themselves even to the toughest and the strongest, it is hard to maintain the ability to smile, let alone laugh.

Duncan and Mrs Dudgeon will, I am sure, bring light and laughter to whoever opens this book. I have no doubt that it will help those who struggle with burdens apparently too heavy to carry, and inform those who are fortunate enough to be well but are looking in on adversity. Make no mistake, it will deeply affect you; it may move you to tears, it may challenge you, but above all, I believe it is a book which will bring hope.

Whether or not one has had the experience of serious illness, or of being in hospital, '*Crutch*' contains a series of life lessons: about finding strength in times of trouble; about the importance of true friendship; about the nature of courage; about facing up to matters of life and death; and ultimately, about the human capacity for laughter, even when it has to fight its way through the tears.

This book is a microcosm of the very best of real life. Indeed, *it is true life*, in that it is based on very real events. Things similar to this *do* happen, each and every day, to unsuspecting people going about their normal lives. I'm told that every year, over thirty thousand women in the UK alone discover they have breast cancer, and goodness only knows how many people suffer with chronic back or hip problems. It is this that makes it such a valuable book to read, and its messages such important ones for us all. I am delighted to be associated with it, and with CancerBACUP and Macmillan Cancer Relief, both of which we hope will benefit greatly from the book's sales. I wish it great success.

Minnie Driver
January 2001
Los Angeles

1

Be warned! When a surgeon says, 'You might be a bit uncomfortable the day after the operation,' he actually means, 'You will feel like nothing on earth.'

What he should have said is that I would spend the first night with a screaming agony at the bottom of my back; the sort of indescribable boiling, searing pain which not only makes one wary of turning over (an impossible feat anyway, unless you intend to throttle yourself on a mass of cables and tubes) but leaves one in fear of moving an eyelid lest the vibrations set off another wave of pain, resulting in a series of unrepeatable expletives rending the calm atmosphere of a night-time hospital corridor. I imagine that if he actually forewarned his patients, he would have a great number of last-minute cancellations – far too many to be able to keep up his membership of the Portuguese golf club.

Actually, I did sleep. The sort of on-off sleep induced by veins full of ebbing anaesthetic which one wishes would never go away because it's far more pleasant to stay in the post-operative never-never land in which you cannot believe that you walked into the room twelve hours previously in moderate discomfort and willingly undertook a procedure which resulted in this torture. And when I did sleep, an apparition in blue kept passing through my dreams, holding my wrist and clunking something noisily onto the end of the bed. I never worked out why she was selling pineapples in the middle of the night. Perhaps she wasn't. Perhaps I dreamed it all. What I did not dream is that she really did wake me at about ten past four in the morning and ask me if I wanted something to help me sleep. People joke about that, don't they? Being woken in the middle of the night when the drugs trolley comes around, only to be offered a sleeping draught.

I remember straining to focus on the timer of the television sitting on its bracket on the opposite wall. '04.10' it flashed. I should have said 'Yes'. I should also have said, 'I'd be grateful if you'd ask the armoured patrol car, the one with the caterpillar tracks which keeps driving across me, to kindly take himself and practise somewhere else.'

'Don't forget your PCA. It's right here beside your hand.'

PCA? What's PCA? More drifting sleep. Then a vague recollection. Press the button; that's what they had said. 'All you will have to do is to press the button and it will feed pain relief into your arm.'

Click ... click, click, click.

Headiness. Understanding looms vaguely through the fog. Press the button when you are in pain. They had explained it all. Click.

When I woke it was light. Not just light, but a dazzling, eye-splitting sunray invaded my senses. Then there was an odour. It smelt like the cat after a bad night on the shed roof.

It's me. My own breath. Far worse than the cat. Come to think about it, my tongue feels like the shed roof too. Water. Reach for the glass.

'Aaaaaah!'

Forget the water.

The door opens and a different figure bustles in; still in blue, but without pineapples this time.

'How do you feel this morning, my love?'

I try to speak. A strange, raucous croak emits where a fine baritone used to be.

'Drink.'

'Mmm?'

I point to my mouth as though I might have toothache, and the blue lady holds the glass to my parched lips.

'Just a little to begin with, luvvie. Not too much.'

Not too much? I need gallons. I need torrents of ice-cold,

2

soothing mountain stream to cool my tongue, to lubricate the bits which were working so well as I quipped with the anaesthetist and counted to ten ... three, actually. I managed to count to three. There's something quite unreal about that moment. I recall having the silly idea that I would get to ten, just to show them; or perhaps it wouldn't work at all and then ... oh my God, no. I don't want to stay awake! 'Two. Three. Fffoo...' Then blankness. Nothing. Fear gone. Time lost, never to be lived. A gap of black, ending in the pain and the snoozing and ... pineapples.

'Pineapples! I think we were dreaming, love. No one came in with pineapples. Funny the things you dream after an op.'

More bustling.

'You can have some breakfast when you feel up to it. Fancy trying some?'

'Please. Yes.'

Thoughts of the whole works. Bacon, egg, Cumberland sausage, lightly grilled tomatoes ... nausea rises somewhere in the middle of me.

'Perhaps not after all. A fruit juice. A cold fruit juice, please.'

It's warm and ... it's pineapple. No it isn't. What's happened to my taste buds? It's orange ... tomato?

'Thank you.'

The effort is overwhelming. Sink back onto the pillows. Lie flat, relax. Click... Hmm. Click.

I thought you may like to know how I fared in that great hospital, imprisoned as I was in the orthopaedic ward. When I say *imprisoned as I was*, I was, of course, not actually imprisoned there against my will. I just thought I would mention that, lest you think that I might be not quite right ... that I might have been residing in some form of high-security unit; the sort of place where no bedside headphones are provided and the bedpans are made of waxed cardboard in case I hung myself from the television bracket or struck myself viciously over the head in an attempt to end my days in that place where everyone calls you 'luvvie', and morphine is available at the proverbial touch

3

of a button. I have to admit if I wanted to end my days any-where, and I don't, because I enjoy them too much, that might be the place to do it in comfort and serenity. Believe it or not, I actually grew to like it. Once I had mastered the art of 'Patient-Controlled Analgesia'(I knew you would want to know what it was) I found I could, at the slightest twinge of discomfort, drift away into a state of euphoric bliss.

Needless to say, they took away my toy. They *'popped it out'*. In hospital, if you have ever had the misfortune to be in one, they do absolutely everything by *'popping'*. It became some-thing of an obsession to me, not that I would ever have dreamt of saying it to any of them, for I'm sure they would have been terribly offended, but a smile would creep across my face every time I received attention from one of the ladies in blue.

'Just *pop* on the bed,' they said when I arrived for my first pre-surgery check-up; 'Just *pop* this around your arm (luvvie),' the nurse said when she first took my blood pressure, the first of seven hundred times before I left; '*Pop* this in,' (thermo-meter), '*Pop* this under you'(bedpan), '*Pop* this out'(i), (removing the bedpan when I had performed), not to mention '*Pop* this out'(ii), a delicate little operation performed in my pyjama front before I managed to fill the er ... bottle, and so on, the latter being the most extraordinary one of all. Can you imagine saying that under any other circumstances – '*Pop it out'*??

Doctors, I hasten to add, never say this. It is nurse-speak designed to minimise the impact of the whole state of affairs, to reduce the loss of dignity resulting from all that they do as they busy themselves around one's body, usually, I should point out without wishing to be in any way distasteful, one's orifices.

Anyway, they took away my morphine, *popping* the line out of my hand. I must admit to having had a twinge of panic at that point. Having had my beloved drugs taken away, I felt rather as a toddler must do come the day the reins are left behind and the child totters out for a first walk, discovering that if he strains forward, gravity takes over, resulting in an almighty crash to the pavement. I wondered if I would cope, but I was reassured; tablets would follow whenever I asked for them and, as if to distract me, again just like a child who has been deprived of some beloved but unhealthy toy, a new figure in blue and white appeared in my life, bearing a Zimmer frame.

There is something quite extraordinary about being presented with one's first frame. As the aid is so closely associated with elderly frailty, it had never occurred to me that I might ever be asked to make use of one before my forty-seventh birthday hove into view. It was the final insult, that first slow walk down the corridor, hospital visitors stepping politely aside, the physiotherapist's hand hovering near my arm while she made encouraging noises.

'That's it. You are doing *wonderfully*! Not too fast now. We don't want to fall, do we?'

'We?' We are not going to fall, are we? I mean, *I am*. It will be me, I thought, who will splurge along the corporate-image carpet, stitches splitting open like a Velcro fastener, insides spilling out ... fortunately it's probably all 'Scotchgarded' against such an eventuality.

As the days passed, and my muscles decided that they might oblige by returning to somewhere near their former strength, I dreamed of escape. (This brings me back to my first point about being imprisoned, you understand.) I did actually dream that I was escaping one sunny afternoon during *rest time*. I dreamed that I was away down the long woodland drive, nearly at the gates, the rubbers on my frame worn away from the unaccustomed treatment on the tarmac surface when ... I was recaptured by a posse of nurses with wheelchairs. '*Pop in here*,' they all chorused tunefully as I sank gratefully into a chair for my reincarceration. Needless to say, it wasn't the rubbers on the frame which were exhausted, it was me and if you have ever had the misfortune to be so indisposed, you will understand that feeling. The sheer exhaustion of doing the smallest task brings total fatigue. The sort of fatigue which renders one so tired that it is impossible even to *think* about going to sleep for the effort required is too great. That's how I was in those first few days. Standing gratefully at the sink to wash (no more of those awful bedbaths which give the staff inexhaustible opportunities for *popping*), I found myself reeling with exhaustion. The very act of lifting a razor to my face brought upon me waves of head-spinning, physical defeat.

'Don't worry. We will feel like that for a few days.'

That *we* again. *We* won't feel exhausted. *I* will. You look remarkably rosy to me and, judging by the gusto with which you applied that flannel about my tender parts a few days ago, I cannot think for a second that you are feeling remotely weary.

The days passed, and finally there was talk of release; I beg your pardon, being allowed home; what they call *discharge* in hospitals, an unfortunate term which I have always more closely associated with ... well, all sorts of unpleasant things like 'Greenaid' campaigns around smelly sewage outfalls; you know the sort of thing, where they half-fly, bouncing across the waves, in those wonderful inflatable little boats, defying officials who are attempting to prevent the crew hanging banners from the pipe gushing the filthy excrement. And boils. They discharge too.

Anyway I was discharged, one sunny day in December, and found myself at home again with Mrs Dudgeon, not believing the exhausted state I had achieved by walking to the waiting car and then making the short journey from car to living room, where I flopped down and immediately wished I was back in hospital. I have never understood this phenomenon. In hospital, one longs for privacy, for real tea, served hot without too much milk as Mrs D makes it, for the right to lock the toilet door and sit on the WC without a voice calling, '*Are we all right in there, Mr Dudgeon?*' and of course, to be able to sing in one's own bathroom. The truth now, have you ever sung in a hospital bathroom? The answer must be 'No'.

But miss it I did. I missed the bustling, the routines, the curious security of it all and, yes, I missed the '*popping*' too. As I collapsed in the armchair and my gaze took in the familiar room, which for some reason seemed twice as spacious as normal, I turned to my desk with its comfortable chair and there, waiting for me, was my word processor.

2

The trouble with owning boats is that they tend to require prodigious amounts of maintenance. Some would say that is why boats are kept. 'Messing about in boats' suggests idyllic afternoons beside the river; sunhats and chilled wine, an occasional dabble with a paintbrush and just ... well, generally enjoying oneself.

Unfortunately, our boat, *Hercules*, is a long boat. That is, a narrowboat which is very long. I say 'unfortunately' only because of the upkeep it demands and perhaps because of the occasional sharp bend in the canal which always seems to have been deliberately constructed with a radius three feet shorter than our old carrying boat can manage. In every other instance its length is a pure pleasure, allowing Mrs Dudgeon and me to have the space to enjoy life afloat to the full without the disadvantages of small boats, which require tables to be collapsed and converted into beds each evening, showers to be folded away to form kitchens and other time-consuming, irritating fiddles which for us diminish the pleasure of being aboard. Dare I say it, there have been occasions when the seventy-two feet of boat have provided the quintessential distance for marital harmony to flourish – usually, I hasten to add, when I am suffering from some withdrawal symptoms occasioned by neither of us remembering to buy teabags or pipe tobacco. Those who know me will immediately understand the far-reaching and unreasonable consequences of such an oversight. I retire to the back cabin and Mrs D sits in the bow. However, the story begins at one of those rare times when we were most certainly not afloat. We were in dry dock. Let me explain.

Every few years, the boat needs to be taken out of the water, cleaned and then recoated with a tar-like paint to protect the steel. To do this one books a few days in the dock. The dock is usually a short length of canal or river, terminating ideally in a boatshed, from which the water can be pumped out, leaving the boat standing on wooden supports. It seems easy, and is, unless you happen to own a boat such as ours which, being old, has dimensions barely suited to the silted canals of today. Modern craft of shallow draught can cruise unfettered by what is sometimes described as the 'bottom being too near the top'; a quaint phrase which I have thought, more than once, also serves to describe Mrs Dudgeon, who is, shall we say, quite short. Bless her.

On the designated afternoon, we stood watching as a sleek, modern narrowboat slid effortlessly out of the dock, steered by a very upright man who looked curiously out of place, dressed as he was in a neatly pressed shirt, polished boat shoes and an immaculate pair of chinos. On his head was a dark blue cap emblazoned with the logo 'Captain'. His progress out of the dry dock was quite rapid. As is often the case with those who bear caps with gold braid, boat-handling proficiency did not match emblazoned decoration, for he could not manoeuvre out of the basin in time and his vessel struck the jetty opposite before ricocheting sideways and then gliding serenely away up the canal, its shiny, black bitumened hull bearing a long, tell-tale scar of the collision. We averted our smiling faces as the 'Captain' disappeared, remonstrating with his wife, who was presumably supposed to have averted the collision in some superhuman way. Somewhat smugly we slowly turned our bow into the restricted opening which would soon be staunched off to allow the dock to be emptied, and all went well until the deepest part of boat, the stern, was in the opening and then it stopped. It gave me the feeling that we had hit a mountain of old rice pudding. The ancient engine spluttered a little, coughed black smoke, and I reversed to have another go at slightly higher speed. The same thing happened again, except that this time the deceleration was a little more abrupt and accompanied by the unmistakeable sound of breaking glass in the galley. Mrs

Dudgeon hastened below, one hand clasped over her mouth. When I tried to go backwards again, nothing happened. A few seconds spent plunging the murky water with a boat hook revealed that we were no longer on the mud, but in it, and all sense of floating had ceased. We were stuck fast.

Various hangers-on appeared at that moment. I am not sure if there is a law to govern the number of worthless suggestions which can be made in a crisis; if there isn't, there should be, for all present made contradictory proposals as to how to proceed. One, a marine surveyor who should have known better, took a long pole and placed it on the curved stern and pushed. Not surprisingly, the pole slipped and his heavy, grunting mass did a neat forward somersault into the water. Chuckling at his own foolhardy behaviour, he clambered cheerfully from the dock and went off to change, only to reappear a little while later and repeat exactly the same procedure, this time from the other side. At that point he retired looking crestfallen, presumably to change at home, having exhausted his supply of dry clothes. Astonishingly, a bystander told us he had done the very same thing the week before. Some people just never seem to learn.

The patient yard owner, having met the problem before, began to bring sacks of coal from the winter fuel stockpile and instructed us to load them tidily onto the bow. When the stack was about fourteen bags high, and coming perilously close to toppling into the canal, he indicated that we should pull on the front mooring line. The stern, now lifted by the sheer leverage of the load on the opposite end, drifted quietly into place and was made fast, the water was pumped out, and an hour later the boat rested on its timber bearers. It's all so easy when you know how.

Mrs Dudgeon made a very large pot of tea for everyone, and I donned waterproofs before beginning to blast weed and rust from the dripping hull with a monster of a machine which seemed to have a mind of its own. The high-pressure washer is a marvellous gadget but one which, if used incorrectly, can not only deposit gallons of water onto the operator but also anything else which happens to be free to fly around. Thus it

10

was that every few minutes a momentary lack of concentration would see me covered in shards of old paint, freshwater mussels, slimy green weed and showers of speckly rust which seemed to attach themselves to my face in successive microscopic layers and then set hard. One's instinctive reaction when this happens is to point the ferocious jet at the floor which, of course, immediately lifts all the filth from the floor and sticks it back onto the side of the boat. Hull cleaning is such a joy – and the pleasure continued for about seven hours until every scrap of loose muck had been blasted away and lay on the dock floor. Mrs Dudgeon supplied endless cups of tea and contributed by occasionally pointing out rust spots I had missed.

It is very curious being inside a boatshed aboard one's boat. It is gloomy throughout the day, and the boat has a hollow resonance being out of the water. It is an unpleasant, unnatural experience which even unsettled the dog. That night, the pump which kept the floor of the dry dock free of leaking water gurgled and periodically gushed. As often happens, I had barely noticed it during the day, but as I lay in our narrow bed listening to the preparatory rumblings followed by a sudden crashing vomit of water into the depth of the canal outside, I found myself counting in a bid to find sleep. Sixty-two or sixty-three seconds between heaves. Eventually I must have fallen asleep, only to be awoken by loud voices echoing in the shed as the neighbouring boat's crew made their uncertain way back from the pub. Doors and side hatches slammed shut, and for the next hour I lay there in the darkness listening to our neighbours' magnified, echoing voices reverberating in the hollowness of the boatshed.

I am sure that they must have been oblivious to the fact that I could hear every detail of their conversation as they prepared their nocturnal supper. A girl spoke as she chopped vegetables, and a man began to sing, accompanied by the inane squeaking of their dog's toy. When I had very nearly had enough and was about to go across and bang something heavy on the roof of their boat, the noise abated as quickly as it had begun, lights went out and silence reigned once more in the gloomy interior of the shed. I lay again listening to the rumbling and gurgling

11

of the pump. Sixty-five seconds ... seventy ... seventy-five; the periods between emptying grew longer and longer. Then I realised with a sudden surge of adrenalin that the pump might be failing and the dry dock refilling. I shot up in bed alarmed, straining to hear the irritating but by now familiar, reassuring symphony of sounds which would be the precursor to the ... gushhh. Relief. I sank back onto my pillow and only then realised that Mrs D had slept soundly throughout.

The next morning, I awoke unusually early, made tea and noisily crashed a few side hatches open while whistling a loud and very tuneless folksong.

Within an hour, I assembled large brushes, a sizeable drum of pitch and set to, beginning the blacking at the bow, only inches away from the heavy timbers which held back the water outside. It is at these times that one realises just how big a large narrowboat is, a fact which is reinforced as the water in the dock recedes to reveal the whole of the hull, normally out of sight beneath the water. As I painted, I found myself passing the time of day by computing how many square feet of hull were to be blacked and then as I calculated what seventy-two feet of hull length, of height about six feet, with two sides and three coats, came to, a voice from behind me spoke, almost echoing my thoughts. I paused, a large black brush gripped in rubber-gloved hand dripping ooze onto the floor.

It was none other than Alfred, Mrs Dudgeon's brother. I refrain from writing 'my brother-in-law', which of course he is; simple loathing forbids. I would, quite simply, prefer not to be personally associated with him in any way whatsoever. Familial ties notwithstanding, he is the laziest man I have ever met, and he happens to live near to the area where we enjoy much of our boating.

We once took him and his wife, Dorothy, for a few days cruise, and I vowed never to be party to such a venture again. For three days Alfred and Dorothy sat in the bow of the boat, waiting for meals and refreshments to be brought to them, and even managed to do the unthinkable: remain onboard while Mrs Dudgeon struggled to work the boat through a series of locks. At one point, Alfred stood up in the bow as we entered a lock and in a booming voice proclaimed to the world, 'About four feet to go, Dunc; three feet, two, whoa!' which is the most straightforward way known to insult a competent narrowboat skipper who has been negotiating canal locks, without assistance, for years. I also have a pathological loathing of being called 'Dunc'.

You will therefore sympathise with me, I hope, if I tell you that when I heard the voice behind me whistle and declare, 'That's a lot of painting you've got to do, Dunc,' and I gripped the brush, imagining all the alternative uses it might be put to, I was not being unreasonable or overreacting.

I turned and, with the merest hint of a smile, suggested that four hands would make lighter work of it and that I had spare Wellington boots and overalls to hand, knowing full well that my offer would fall on stubbornly deaf ears.

'Thanks, but no. Looks like hard work to me. I think I'll just sit outside in the sun and read my paper. Have you got a deckchair on board?'

Then as he turned away, he paused. 'There's a small patch there that you've missed.'

Mrs D appeared at that point and, sensing that in a very short while all would not be well, indeed that her brother might soon be found floating face down in the canal, she gave me a strong cup of tea, my pipe and tobacco, and removed Alfred from my presence on some pretext or other.

It took three days to complete the task, and during this time, while the bitumen was drying between coats, I took advantage of the covered dock to do other painting jobs. Each year I have tried to paint *Hercules'* roof, a not insignificant task as it is just under sixty feet long and nearly six feet wide. It is almost impossible to do this without kneeling; first to sand it down, and then to degrease it before painting it in the traditional red oxide. And here we come to the point of the story. The effect of kneeling while I completed these three tasks was marked. I found I was becoming increasingly sore around my back and hip, and the more I knelt, the worse it became. By the time I had finished and washed my brushes clean, I was limping around the boatyard and feeling not a little sorry for myself. The now-dry thousand square feet of hull beckoned, however, and after a well-earned lunch, which included one of Mrs Dudgeon's excellent apple pies and a pint of local bitter from the nearby pub, I again climbed wearily down the steps into the dock.

Beginning a coat of paint on such a vast surface is daunting, but the tar can be applied with surprising rapidity. What I discovered was that the low parts, reached by kneeling on a board strategically placed on the wet floor, were apparently becoming lower; either that or I was bending less easily. That the latter was true became very obvious as I rounded the stern and tried to lay beneath it to apply preservative above my head. I extracted myself in misery and discomfort as the pain in my back and leg increased. I will never know how *Hercules'* last side was finished, but the following morning I was greatly relieved to see the eddies of water swirling around the hull again and to feel the gentle rocking one associates with being afloat once more. We drew carefully out of the dock, taking care to avoid the jetty, where the last boat to leave had left a long, black smudge.

3

I cannot imagine why anyone would wish to throw himself out of an aeroplane. It is a complete mystery to me, and yet it is very clear that enthusiasts are obsessed with it and queues of new converts wait in the wings (so to speak). Magazines actually advertise 'Once in a lifetime opportunities for your loved one'. The organisations invite you to learn to drive a steam train, take circuits at racecourses at breakneck speeds in a racing car, or hurl yourself out of a plane at 6,000 feet. The notion that anyone might feel it is appropriate to give such a present to a cherished husband is, frankly, deeply suspicious.

Why would one do this? It seems to me to be on a par with taking out a loaded Smith and Wesson on the loved one's birthday morning and saying, 'Darling, guess what I have bought for you; it's a new game called Russian Roulette.' It would be preposterous and yet, if the advertising claims are to be believed, hundreds, thousands even, will, with the most elementary training, be willing to leap off the wing of a high-flying plane in order to plummet earthwards while his or her spouse watches from below. Happy birthday, Sweetheart.

I have to confess to having a slight bias here. I was one of the unfortunate ones whose parachuting experiences were not entirely wholesome. They were, without wishing to exaggerate, the most sick-making, terrifying events of my entire life, and about as charming as meeting a heavily loaded juggernaut hurtling towards you on the wrong carriageway of the London Orbital. The jump which went wrong was, and here is the relevance of this tale, the first time I injured my back, and I had more or less forgotten about it until I sat with a doctor who was examining the detailed scans of my spine. He poured over dozens of images spread out on his desk, like a dendrochronologist studying the freshly sawn stump of a tree.

'Hmm. That's a good one. Judging by the graininess it's very old damage. A long time ago.'

I expected him to begin commenting on the rainfall that year – 'I can see there wasn't much water that summer. A bit crinkly' – but he didn't. Instead he asked when my bad back had begun.

I have to tell you all the truth, I cannot actually remember a time when I have not had a bad back. Most of us have suffered at some time, usually on a Sunday evening after a long bout of digging the garden, but a good night's rest usually solves the problem until the following year, when the sun shines again and we are tempted to repeat the folly once more.

As I sat in the consulting room, where the bespectacled doctor scribbled rapidly on a notepad, I was caused to reflect. He raised his eyebrows as I catalogued the occasions when my back had suffered as result of some overzealous activity, either on a narrowboat or during the rebuilding of the uninhabitable barn Mrs Dudgeon and I had once chosen to live in.

'You haven't given it much of a chance, have you?'

He smiled and his gaze returned to the images.

I stretched out further on my right side in the now all-too-familiar posture I was used to adopting so that no weight was carried on the painful side.

'There was the parachuting, of course.'

He paused, pen still in the air.

'Go on.'

I told him briefly about my 'unfortunate experience', but for the sake of the reader who may not understand my complete aversion to anything to do with aeroplanes, it is only proper to tell the tale in full. Forgive me, but these things matter.

At the age of about eighteen, when schools still had real military cadet units which allowed one to play soldiers or sailors to one's heart's content, I, along with a couple of others, went to the West Country to spend a week at a parachute training camp. My recollections of the week are hazy except that, owing to a painful ingrowing toenail which was to receive surgery on my return, I had had a penicillin injection in my behind the day before. Railway carriage seats in those days were of heavy moquette, always with a characteristically dusty smell and particularly robust springs. I remember that cushion very well. The corridor coach, arranged in compartments with individual sliding doors, allowed me to sit in very private misery. My rear end smarted with every jolt all through the journey, such was my bruise from an overzealous, syringe-bearing nurse. All I recall is how hard those seats were and how long it took to reach Yeovil. I was black and blue before we arrived at the station, where we climbed into the back of a large army truck which, of course, had very hard wooden benches. Considering the purpose of the expedition, you will appreciate that I did not arrive at the camp in prime parachuting condition.

Repeated parachute drills and fall practice from scaffolding towers did nothing for my behind, or the mounting anxiety which grew within me as the day of the first jump drew closer. When the appointed time arrived, the flight was postponed several times due to low cloud, and we sat in a particularly miserable mess room and quaked. We all made regular visits to the lavatory and then, suddenly, there was a break in the weather, and before we knew it, we were airborne and hooking ourselves to the fixed cords, eyes glued on an amber light glowing on the bulkhead above the tiny opening where the wind screamed past. Then we were pushed to the plane's door by a jump instructor who yelled, 'When I say go, go! Right?' ... 'Go! Go! Go!' and with each command a frightened teeenager plummeted earthwards.

I can still conjure up the feeling of floating downwards having made all the checks: count, canopy open and filled, correct hand placement. Even today I frequently dream about it, usually accompanied by a heavy, cold sweat. It all passed so quickly that it was barely possible really to relax and enjoy it before the earth raced towards one's feet. Then it was all over and we were concentrating on following the correct drill to

17

gather in the 'chute before a Land Rover raced up to collect the widely scattered novice jumpers.

I cannot recall which jump went wrong or how I coped. It is as if the memory has been erased, possibly by the sheer terror of the moment, but in short, my parachute did not open. To be precise, the first one did not and the reserve one did. Staring upwards at a failing parachute which is streaming in the air as uselessly as a string vest on a washing line was, I believe, one of my life's most sobering moments. The time interval between the two events was such that valuable hundreds of feet of slowing-down time were lost. This was the occasion when the ground really did hurtle up to meet me. What I had experienced before on previous jumps seemed, by comparison, to be slow motion. I was terrified. No words will suffice to relate quite how that felt. I recall descending with a continuous groan issuing from my lips. If there was no time to think previously, there was certainly less now. The various drills flashed through my mind but at the last moment, I was all arms and legs flailing helplessly, braced at-the-ready too early and then missing the crucial point of impact. All I can recall about it was the spine-jarring thump, the instantaneous deceleration which left my head feeling as though it was springing up from somewhere near to my appendix, and then a ground crew hauling me to my feet and bundling me into the pick-up truck.

I hurt. My feet hurt, my back hurt, my neck hurt and my brain felt as though someone had taken repeated, athletic swipes at my skull with a tennis racket. My lip was bleeding where I had bitten it, and I felt very sorry for myself.

It is important to understand how little scope there is for feeling sorry for oneself in the forces. The word 'sympathy' does not exist in HM Forces Regulation Issue Dictionary. A senior instructor who towered above us slapped me on the back and barked congratulatory words.

'Good lad! Good lad! Remembered it all, didn't we? Shame about the final seconds. You were doing well. There'll be an enquiry about the 'chute, but up again tomorrow morning so you don't lose your nerve, lad. Right, come over 'ere you lot.

Fall in. Now then, Dudgeon's done well. Who could see what was happening from above? Nelson. Did you see his landing? What went wrong, eh?'

I did jump the next day, but I had already lost my nerve. I did it perfectly, but my stomach felt like a bowl of half-set jelly during the descent, and despite falling well and achieving a perfect configuration at touchdown, there were sparks of electricity from my back as I hit the ground. Needless to say, I never jumped again. Unbeknown to me at the time, I had achieved the first damaged disc in my back, although I was not to discover it until later. Much, much later.

'Did you have any treatment at the time?'

'Er, no.' Parachute regiments did not offer 'treatment'.

I went to bed on an ancient, sagging iron-frame bed that must have seen service in the Second World War, if not the First one, and spent the long night in silent agony. The next day I went back on the train. The seats were no softer and my behind was bruised. When I tell you that my behind was bruised, I do mean just that; my behind was bruised. All of it.

4

It is a curious thing but, despite all the terrible abuse I had hurled at my back, the final straw which convinced me that I could not cope was an insignificant affair.

In the previous decade, I once heaved the boat's huge batteries out of the engine room and managed to prostrate myself on the towpath in the pouring rain. They were not normal batteries, I hasten to add, but American batteries originating from the USAF, which used them in warplanes in banks of six to provide adequate voltage. They weighed nearly as much as a man and they were indestructible. I was not, however, and my spine shrank another few millimetres as I lifted one of them out of the boat as an expedient move to avoid seeking assistance or hiring an expensive crane.

On another occasion, I spent no less than three weeks plastering a ceiling, which as you may guess indicates that either the plasterer was very slow or the ceiling extremely large. It was probably both, but the ceiling was unusually extensive. It was a barn ceiling, and for three weeks I mixed plaster in the yard, carted it up the stairs, up a ladder and onto the scaffolding where it was applied, and the whole process repeated every ten minutes or so until I had used no less than two tonnes of plaster. It was madness.

The fact is that we all have an element of what Mrs D calls 'the Wally Factor'. I know exactly what she means. However, I am convinced that our capacity to act, on occasions, as complete Wallies is part of our essential genetic inheritance. I say this because my mother has a very strong Wally Factor and so does my father. The trait manifests itself in different ways, but it is there in the Dudgeon family and it is passed on from one generation to the next.

In a different context, the Wally Factor is probably responsible for extraordinary feats of bravery on the battle field or impressive action in crisis situations. I am sure that if you were to research the genes of those who have been awarded Victoria Crosses, you would discover that all possess the Wally Factor, and those who were awarded it posthumously would, without doubt, have had it in double portion. Therefore, far from being a negative aspect of our personalities, I see it as an essential requisite for the survival of the human race. Without it, we would doubtless all spend most of our time snoozing our lives away in armchairs and our war histories would be littered with examples of indecision and fecklessness. Admiral Lord Nelson, instead of rousing the crews of the fleet with his signal, 'England expects every man to do his duty,' would have run flags up to the effect that 'Every man should at least give some thought to the aforementioned battle, but for those who do not wish to partake, a video of *Sportsnight* highlights will be shown on the Poop Deck at noon.' Believe me, if the Wally Factor has not yet been discovered by geneticists, it soon will be.

I remember a piece of extreme and ignominious foolishness many years ago, which may well account for Damaged Disc number two. As is often the case, there was no reason to have acted with such unnecessary gusto – but I did. The Wally Factor was at work.

When I began my career as a teacher, it coincided with the year of ROSLA. This acronym stood for 'Raising of the School Leaving Age' when, instead of leaving at fifteen years of age, pupils had to remain for one further year leaving at sixteen. Not surprisingly, the particular cohort in question were seething with resentment at being 'caught' in the bureaucracy of change, and they made sure that those of us who had to teach them knew it. I am not quite sure what I had done to deserve 5Z on Wednesdays, but we suffered each other for no less than six lessons, which was most of the day. The truth was that nearly

21

everyone else on the staff had refused to teach them, and actually, to be fair to the pupils, we struck up a rough rapport and at times enjoyed ourselves. The powers that be had agreed that rather than teach normal classroom lessons to this motley group of twenty-five malingerers and malcontents, I would work out of doors and attempt to share with them some of the basic skills of garden landscape and design.

At the end of one very tiring day, my patience worn to a ravelling, I tried in vain to persuade them to finish off the task in hand, and in a moment of sheer exasperation, picked up a railway sleeper and threw it across the site. I feel honour bound to tell you that it was aimed at a group of particularly motionless, feckless individuals, but I missed. Now I am sure that to those who regularly participate in the Highland Games and fling cabers around as a matter of course, the act would seem insignificantly puny, but for me it signalled a period of prolonged bed rest. However, that was not itself the act of foolishness.

A little later, quite breathless with pain, I walked slowly home, as only those who have suffered from a bad back will understand, and on the way passed a rubbish skip beside the road which contained amongst other things, a large door. My ambition at that moment was to lie as still and flat as possible while Mrs D looked after my every need, so I went to the house which seemed to be amassing rubbish in the skip, and asked if I might have the door. It seemed very logical when I did it, and I duly set off up the hill, carrying my briefcase in one hand and the door, which was destined for the base of my bed, balanced in the other. The effort required was immense, and by the time I pressed the door bell and Mrs Dudgeon let me in, I was groaning audibly with every step. I crawled up the stairs on hands and knees while my wife and a friendly neighbour carried the door up to the bedroom, lifted the mattress and inserted it. Such was my discomfort that I managed to make my way on all fours to the bed, where my capable friend lifted me slowly and with infinite care onto the bed and then, with a bewildered shake of his head, left the room.

* * *

These examples might give you a little idea of the influence of the W-gene although for many of you, those of you who possess it, such explanations will be unnecessary. You will already be completely familiar with the sort of behaviour it can induce. If you have not yet begun to suffer physically as a result of the W-gene driven abuse you will undoubtedly wreak on yourself one day, then I strongly suggest that you check out the levels of medical insurance you carry because, believe me, you will need it.

The straw which finally broke the camel's back was not at all exciting. Oh that it could have been! It was in fact one of the most domestic events possible; far from skiing off-piste slopes or swinging on a chimney whilst installing a new flue liner, either of which could have upset my back but did not, I was doing nothing more significant than opening the fridge door at the time.

Precariously balanced in the fridge was a bowl of leek and potato soup, the remains of a hurried lunch. As I opened the door, the bowl slipped forwards, falling towards the floor, and in an attempt to save the dish from smashing, I raised my foot, hoping to catch it or at least break its fall. What actually happened was that I achieved a magnificent drop-kick which launched the bowl back into the fridge, where it hit the shelf, splattering the contents all over the inside of the cabinet. Simultaneously I felt something move sharply in my back. I sat on the floor, staring in dismay at the soup which slowly dripped through all the shelves.

If you have ever spilled potato soup, you will know that it is the most glutinous of substances, covering everything with a robust film which defeats all attempts at cleaning. Milk bottles, packs of bacon and cheese, salads and cold food dripped silently as the soup slowly percolated through the extremes of the fridge.

Mrs Dudgeon was out at the time, so although I could no longer kneel, I scoured the whole cabinet as best I could, but all my efforts to remove the grainy film were in vain. Leek and potato soup sticks like billy-ho, and I am now in the process of patenting it as a shoe-repairing adhesive. I am sure it will be an astounding success – and for those of you who care about environmental matters, note that it is of course entirely organic. When Mrs Dudgeon enquired about the remains of the soup the next day, I told her, quite truthfully, that there was a very small amount left and that it was in the fridge.

5

Shortly after the soup-kicking incident I decided that enough was enough. Not only was my back now painful all of the time, but a new discomfort, one I had rarely experienced before I blacked *Hercules'* bottom, was affecting my entire leg, making it difficult to walk. Mrs D and the children had been quite disturbed by a new phenomenon, which was my inability to sit at the table and eat a meal without streaks of fire travelling rapidly from my back to my toes. It was sudden and violent and once or twice resulted in my Cornflakes being flung from a spoon and liberally redistributed across the breakfast table.

If you have suffered from any sort of nerve impingement, you will understand how utterly overwhelming and uncontrollable such a reaction is. It is painful but, I suspect, worse for the sympathetic onlooker, who can only stand and observe their loved one being hurled around as though spasmodically connected to the National Grid by a sadistic torturer.

We were indeed fortunate that, having suffered from a series of ongoing back problems, I was already in touch with an excellent team which had treated me during the previous four or five years. We were also greatly blessed by having decided many years before that, despite the cost, insuring the whole family for private health cover was one of life's essentials. More of this later, but suffice it to say that when we requested an appointment, it was hurriedly arranged and Mrs D drove me gingerly to the hospital where the back team functioned.

Travelling with a bad back is not for the faint-hearted. For the patient, it involves hanging from the ceiling hand-hold with one hand while the other cushions one's bottom from vibrations. I have found that it is very effective to hang from the lip of the open sun roof and disregard what those following in the car behind may think about my behaviour if they happen to notice the orang-utan-like antics in the car in front. The driver of the invalid has to be determinedly brave and just drive, despite the 'Ooohs', 'Aaahs' and other expletives which issue from the passenger seat at intervals as the car travels over the tiniest imperfections in the road surface such as leaves, discarded chewing gum and cigarette ends.

On one occasion when Mrs D was away my daughter, who had recently passed her driving test, kindly offered to take me to the hospital in the old car with which we had equipped her to commute to college. It was a mistake. Hugging the kerb along country lanes meant that we visited every pothole and roadside drain cover for miles around, most of them at breakneck speed, feet from the car in front.

'Could we perhaps slow down a little?' I enquired weakly. 'Ease back from this lorry in front so you do not have to hit the brakes quite so hard perhaps. No darling, your driving is wonderful ... just a little exuberant for me at the moment', and so on.

If you ever have the misfortune to need someone to drive you under these circumstances, do choose carefully. It really does matter. Select the plushest, largest car you can find and make it clear that the driver is not auditioning for a getaway-car part in the movies. Sedateness is the key word, and if the person cannot cope with a stream of traffic waiting impatiently behind, put a notice in the back window. I suggest 'Beware flying vomit ... carsick passenger on board.' It works a treat.

Mrs Dudgeon and I sat patiently outside the consulting room to see a doctor we had not met before. It was high summer, and unfortunately the regular consultants were on holiday. After a short while Dr Richard appeared and called an elderly lady who was sitting near to us with her middle-aged daughter. My heart went out to her, for she was clearly racked with arthritis and shuffled along, barely able to put one foot in front of the other as she progressed with her sticks across the waiting room. Mrs D and I both noticed a hint of impatience on Dr Richard's face as he appeared to make a mental calculation of how long it was going to take the dear old soul to reach his room and be ensconced for her consultation.

'You take your time, Mrs Archibald,' he said in a crisp voice, 'I'll go and read your notes,' and with that he promptly wedged the door open for her and disappeared inside again and sat down at his desk.

When Mrs Archibald and daughter emerged it was our turn, and Dr Richard briefly shook hands and sat at the desk and totally ignored us while he flipped through my quite considerable file. I perched on a chair and looked at Mrs D, wondering whether to take out my pocket chess set and begin a game, when he finally looked up. I should point out that when I described my position as 'perched on a chair', I meant exactly that. I was perched on the arm of the easy chair, being long unable actually to sit in one.

He asked me what was wrong, and I described my symptoms.

'Where do you think the pain is coming from?' he asked abruptly, and I pointed to the general area of my back.

'Around here.'

He looked unmoved as though I had not spoken. He asked me again. I gave the same reply and looked at him. He returned to the notes and thick wallets of images.

'Right, hop up on the couch. Let's have a look at you. You say you knelt while you painted the roof of your boat?'

He asked the question in a manner which was slightly reminiscent of a sarcastic PE teacher I once had the misfortune to be taught by. 'You mean, Dudgeon, you've brought yet another one of your scruffy little off-games notes?' he used to say in his most scornful and belittling tone.

I nodded as I tried desperately to get on the high bed without the aid of the steps conspicuously unavailable just beneath the couch. Having managed this, which felt about equivalent to asking the budgie if he might carry the shopping in, I submitted while he proceeded to carry out a series of tests, by now familiar to me. Mrs Dudgeon averted her gaze being equally familiar with the results.

27

'Aaaah', 'No' and 'Ooooh!' accompanied the rough bending and lifting and rolling of legs.

'Bit stiff? Right. Hop down.'

He reimmersed himself in scan images.

'I think you've got to get fit. How much exercise do you do?'

I replied that I had conscientiously pursued a rigorous daily programme of exercises and stretches as directed by the hospital's physiotherapist.

'No, I mean real exercise,' he said with a slightly scathing tone which suggested less than undying admiration for the sort of regime I had followed. I looked a little blankly at him.

'Pull-ups. Press-ups.'

'No,' I replied, 'I don't do many of those. The physiotherapist said that I should, at all costs, avoid...'

'Listen,' he nearly hissed, 'you're a fit young man. There's nothing much wrong with you,' and he patted the fat file. 'You can't expect to do things like kneel while you paint your boat unless you're fit.'

He emphasised the last word in a manner which made me conclude that he probably road-runs for at least fifteen miles before breakfast every day.

'Fit,' he repeated and then, 'do you know about pain-pathways?'

'Yes I do,' I said, having made it my business to be knowledgeable about managing chronic pain.

'Do you really?' he enquired, with a look which bordered on the menacing and then he reached for his briefcase, took out a piece of headed notepaper and, without checking anything, wrote down the full details of a book, including its reference number. I had the feeling he might have done it once or twice before.

'Read this,' he snapped. 'Meanwhile exercise. How much do you swim?'

I explained that I exercised regularly in the hospital's warm hydrotherapy pool and I saw the same cynical look flit across his face.

'I mean real swimming...'

28

I explained that the water in most swimming pools is so cool that if one's muscles are in a state of irascible tension, it is impossible to exercise fast enough to keep warm and the whole process becomes destructive...

'Pretend it's warm. Just ignore the cold.'

'Right ... ignore the cold.' Of course. Why hadn't *I* thought of that?

At this point I think it is fair to say that Mrs Dudgeon and I were both of one mind; that special sense of togetherness which comes from years of instinctively knowing what the other is thinking took over. We both knew that this was going nowhere and that it could all come to blows if the consultation continued. We both began to edge to the upright and then the door.

'Thank you,' I murmured. 'Thank you.'

A broad beaming smile swept across Dr Richard's face.

'Not at all,' he said. 'Come and see me again if you have any problems at all.'

I nodded, retreating towards the door.

'I will.'

And with that we departed, wondering whether the hospital had run out of funds and somehow induced someone from the accounts department, or perhaps the catering manager, to stand in for the absent consultant. Had they actually done so, I suspect that we would have probably left with far more useful advice.

When we emerged from the Outpatients' Department Mrs D turned to me.

'His name is wrong. It should be Dick,' she said firmly, and from that moment onwards the doctor concerned was never referred to in any other way.

We came away totally dismayed, feeling as though we had been thoroughly cheated of the help we had come to expect from the excellent hospital, and I went home and tried press-ups and pull-ups with the predicted outcome. Afterwards, while I lay on the bed, writhing in discomfort from the exercises, I did at least manage to read the book, entitled simply, *Pain*.

Quite by chance, a few weeks ago, we discovered that our

29

cheerful and charming friend had, surprise, surprise, spent twenty-five years as a doctor in the Forces looking after amongst others, yes, you guessed ... parachute casualties. Nothing changes.

I am sure that of all the doctors in the hospital, Dr Richard has the greatest track record of 'successes' for the simple reason that I cannot imagine anyone at all returning to see him. From this he doubtless concludes that he has sent his patients away armed with the life-enhancing knowledge that, far from being unwell, they are simply deluding themselves and could be healthy again for want of adopting a slightly more realistic outlook towards their sad bodies.

I am also sure that his bill for the consultation, which is beside me on my desk as I write, will remain there, unpaid.

6

I once heard tell of two teenage boys who, being keen to create a marketable designer drug to sell on the streets and being short of glutinous binding substances (not to mention cash), duly raided the local pigeon loft in search of bird dung. Far be it from me to provide recipes for such ventures, but it is interesting to reflect on the fact that these two youngsters were prosecuted, not for the sale of illegal substances, but for the pretence. Amongst the other materials mixed into their money-spinning concoctions were chalk, sink cleaner and paracetamol. All perfectly legal of course, but need I say more ... *caveat emptor*. On the streets they do not come with those tidy, folded little notes which always accompany my medicines.

I have a confession to make. During the last few months I have been taking drugs. Not just once or twice either; lots of them, and in various mixtures, and not the pigeon poo variety, but real ones and worse; drugs to combat the effects of the drugs too.

The problem of extreme, prolonged back pain, weeks and weeks of it, before and during treatment, was ameliorated by the team who swung into action when we asked, somewhat cautiously, for a second opinion, having experimented unsuccessfully with the pull-ups, press-ups and long-distance swims. Having climbed and exhausted most of the 'analgesic ladder', as the pain specialists call the pharmaceutical armoury at their disposal, I started on the opiate look-alikes. These are the painkillers which are nearly as effective as morphine and pethidine, but are popular because they are not quite as addictive. I cannot tell you how relieved I was to be prescribed them, to

31

escape a living hell of agony which would swoop without warning reducing one to a gibbering wreck on the floor, or bed if it happened to be near enough.

The effects were immediate. It was bliss to spend the first twenty-four hours with little more than a few uncomfortable twinges. It seemed unreal, and indeed there is something rather chimerical about such a state. One could be forgiven for believing that not only the symptoms have departed but possibly the causes as well; until the dose begins to wane, that is, and then one is catapulted back to reality with a severe shock (which felt like the mains voltage kind in my case).

I am not usually given to reading the small print on such things as drugs leaflets; I usually only read the sticky label affixed by the chemist. You know the sort of thing: 'To be taken three times daily before or after food'. (Is there any other time, one wonders?) But what about this for small print?

'The side-effects of Z may include feeling sick, being sick, dizziness (especially after standing up from a sitting-down position), a dry mouth, weariness or tiredness, headache, mental confusion, itching or a skin rash, hallucinations or shortness of breath, constipation ... or more unusually (you mean the other ones were usual!) dependence (addiction), feelings of sadness, nervousness or fidgetiness, fits, convulsions, rapid or slow heart beat and increase in blood pressure, sweating...'

Or after taking M, you might expect 'a general increase in muscle tone and involuntary movements may occur. These may cause rhythmic spasms particularly in the face, tongue, jaw or neck. Unusual positioning of the head (??) shoulders or back, slurred speech' ... but you will be pleased to know that 'the majority of these effects are reversible, usually disappearing within 24 hours of stopping treatment.' Well, that's very reassuring.

What about the one, V (prescribed together with Z), which presumably results in simultaneous diarrhoea and constipation? For listed under 'Common Side-Effects' we find: 'stomach pain or discomfort, dizziness, swelling of the legs, and/or feet due to fluid retention, indigestion, heartburn, nausea and ... diarrhoea.'

It's not that I would wish you to think me ungrateful to my doctor who monitored and adjusted my prescription with every possible kindness, but I scored about three out of ten on average (if you will excuse the unintended pun) when it came to side-effects. I didn't begin to consider these tiny folds of paper as anything but humorous until I stood in the bedroom one morning and was convinced I had turned pear-shaped. I hadn't of course, and Mrs D was immensely reassuring on that point; it just seemed as though I had. It really felt as though I was sinking towards the floor – and it was very disconcerting. I was frightened as my centre of gravity descended to below my knees and the top of my body seemed to slim down to something approximating to the thickness of my arm.

Less amusing still was the persistent nausea which swept over me at the most awkward times which, when combined with a distinct inability to run, meant that there were quite a few near misses.

The feelings of anxiety which accompanied the use of these wonderful, carefully researched, rigorously tested analgesics changed my character to the extent that Mrs Dudgeon felt she was living with someone who had no sense of humour. Just imagine that. Instead of my usual cheerful, confident self I was reduced to an anxious, tongue-tied, forgetful, disorganised, clumsy and fairly useless member of my household, and, I may add, my office. The latter experience persuaded me that no matter how I might have struggled physically to meet the demands of my workplace, I knew I had to go sick and to remain at home. I recall one particular morning when I was due to meet some clients and I realised that I was quite unable to do so. I knew this was true not least because at that moment I was hiding in the Gents, peering cautiously around the door, waiting for a colleague to take the good people elsewhere. I had completely, and very alarmingly, lost my nerve for the most straightforward of encounters.

I tell you, it's all true. Of course I also slept, and then there was the terrible morning sickness ... shall I continue?

A word to the young in passing, assuming of course that my

publisher can persuade you to read this book. The point is this: if you put powerful substances into your bodies, don't ever underestimate the short-term and possible long-term effects of doing so. I think you would be extremely foolish to dabble, based on my own, recent experiences of legitimate drugs. The illicit drugs you may be offered on the streets will almost certainly not be pure, chemically-speaking. Most are not, of course. They are 'cut' with everything under the sun. If you are very fortunate, it will be nothing more dangerous than pigeon poo. Lecture over.

The proper management of pain is a wonderful skill for which I will always be grateful. Without it, I am sure I would have stopped moving altogether and in doing so, done myself enormous harm as I physically atrophied into a cabbage-like state. True, that with the analgesics I could hardly manage to answer the phone, read a book or remember the most elementary domestic detail, but the downside was one well worth paying and occasionally even amusing.

Believe it or not, I once got lost, not so very unusual if hiking in the countryside or while on a remote drive, but this was right in the middle of our local town. Mrs Dudgeon had accompanied me everywhere when we went out, which wasn't often, because my range of operation was so short; maybe she had a foreboding of what could happen. On the day in question we decided to go to two separate shops and meet ten minutes later back at the car. I had the car keys as I was likely to be quicker completing my purchases. I went to the supermarket to do nothing more than buy some rawhide chews for the dog, which I did in a couple of moments, and then, remembering that I needed to replace my electric razor before going to hospital, I went to another shop. It took me minutes to select the appropriate model, but about twenty to reach the check-out after the elderly lady before me in the queue attempted the most complicated exchange of gift tokens for her goods.

When I emerged, it was as though a fog had descended on me. My short-term memory was lost and I stared at the hundreds and hundreds of cars, completely unable to remember where Mrs Dudgeon had parked. Eventually I found it, having traversed row upon row, and at that moment a breathless Mrs D saw me and hurried to my side, greatly relieved. It transpired that she had asked numerous friends and acquaintances if they had seen me, and several had affirmed that they had. To ensure that my hitherto sound reputation was left in tatters, she explained about 'my problem'. Their good advice was immediately forthcoming, leaving me in no doubt that the police are often very wise in not seeking information from eye-witnesses. I had apparently been seen sorting through the party accessories counter; looking earnestly at packs of gaily coloured napkins and balloons, said one. Another had seen me at the fresh pasta counter. The wealth of information only served to exacerbate the chaos, as you and I know that all I had done was to buy the dog a bone or two. I have never managed to convince my family that I was not contemplating buying a bag of children's party hats, and my colleagues and neighbours all now pass me with a certain sort of knowing smile. Thank you, Mrs D.

I am quite prepared to admit that once or twice I did make an occasional error about the house. One evening, I offered to prepare the meal, a simple affair of jacket potatoes, salads and fish. I scrubbed and pricked the potatoes, set it all going and went to join Mrs Dudgeon in the sitting room. After a while she asked if the meal might be ready and I duly went to inspect the microwave oven, which, to my consternation and embarrassment, was inexplicably empty. I finally traced the tray of potatoes to the fridge, where they sat quite uncooked and as hard as ever.

The workings of the memory are complex, and there are many poor souls who battle against permanent and profound memory loss. Others suffer temporarily as I did through the administration of mind-altering drugs or sometimes sheer weariness.

A friend of ours once went upstairs in the middle of a dinner party which he and his wife were hosting and, on reaching the landing, could not recall what he had gone for. He went into the bedroom and after a few minutes sat on the chair. After another interval he undressed and went to bed, much to the embarrassment of his wife, who came to look for him after the dessert was finished and he had not reappeared. Personally, I have always believed that he knew exactly what he was doing, but he claims otherwise. I have often felt like doing exactly the same at one of my dear wife's gatherings.

More seriously, a colleague once told me that his ageing father had lost his memory to a staggering proportion and could rarely recall basic information about himself or his family. The son once received an early morning phone call from his mother.

'Come round as soon as you can dear, please. It's your father. He awoke and started shouting at me the moment he opened his eyes. He doesn't know who I am.'

It transpired that the old man had woken, failed to recognise his wife of forty-eight years and accused her of being a loose woman. 'You whore,' he raged, 'get up and leave this house as soon as possible before my wife finds you in her bed.'

When I repeated the story to Mrs Dudgeon, she declared that, without wishing to make merry with the terrible afflictions of others, she could think of numerous advantages to awaking with a different person beside her each morning. I'm sure I don't know what she can mean.

Ah, me. At least my muddled antics were never about anything more than forgetting where the car had been parked. Now then, where did I put that...?

7

'We've stopped, Mr Dudgeon, because we're not getting a clear enough image. You don't have any metal in your underpants, do you?'

'Er no, I don't ... at least not when I last looked,' I assured the radiographer, and then as an afterthought, 'what sort of metal do people have in their underpants, for goodness sake?'

He smiled. 'You'd be surprised. Usually it's a laundry label with tiny amounts of metal in it.'

This was a revelation to me ... how many people send their pants to a laundry?

I was assured that a surprising number of people did, although I've yet to meet one. On the other hand, it's not the sort of thing one would know, is it? Definitely not information one seeks out in social gatherings, is it?

'Oh hello, John. Lovely to see you. Red or white wine? How's the golf and er ... the knickers? All coming back from the laundry well these days?'

'Let's have another go,' the radiographer said, 'it's probably just the machine,' but before we started again, he did actually check my undies for the offending labels.

The MRI scanner is a miracle of modern science. A huge machine, often occupying a suite of rooms, it relies upon very powerful magnetic fields to produce highly detailed images of the internal workings of the body. Its main part is a huge coil into which the patient is introduced, lying quite still on a bed which moves into the drum. If you are claustrophobic, you need to be prepared for the experience, as the walls are quite

37

close to the face and it can seem very confined. The answer is simple: go to sleep. It works every time.

When you arrive they usually show you to a changing room, where you dress in theatre greens or a gown as they do not allow you to go into the machine with your studded jeans on in case the magnetic field rips your trousers apart and flings them all over the room. Usually there is an amusing but necessary questionnaire to complete first in which one declares that one's body is free from shrapnel and other pieces of potential missile-like metal.

I have no fears about the process any longer, although the problem of keeping perfectly still can be difficult if you are in pain. Last time, I took one of my wonderful little tablets a little while before to ensure that I had every chance of being with the fairies throughout. One of the oddest things is that a choice of music is offered via headphones, but every time I have entered the machine the music has been lost for the duration. Presumably nobody has ever thought to tell them that their headphones do not work inside the scanner, and as a result there are, each day, dozens of baffled patients, all wondering why Classic FM has become silent until the last moment, when the bed draws out again and the music begins once more. The relief of being out of the machine is so great that I, along with all the others, have forgotten to say, 'Oh, by the way...'

Inside the machine an intercom keeps one in touch with the technicians, who are safe behind a very stout wall built, presumably, to ensure that if the laundry labels start to break loose from people's underpants, no one gets hurt. I am not convinced that the intercom is a two-way affair. Something about it doesn't quite ring true. Messages come through such as, 'All right, Mr Dudgeon? Ready for another run now? About four minutes this time.'

Until very recently I have always said, 'Yes', no further comment being necessary, but during the particularly long laundry-label session, I replied, albeit in a very timid voice, 'I wouldn't mind coming out to stretch before we...' but the rhythmic dum, dum, dum, dum of the machine started. No one can hear you. You see, it's like the headphones; no one has ever told them.

But don't worry, beside one's waist is a panic button on a long lead. I'm told that if it is pressed, everything will be stopped. Assuming that is, that it all works.

8

Before a surgeon begins spine surgery he will have, ideally, a very clear idea of where the trouble is; a set of map co-ordinates. As our wonderful surgeon, Mr Thomas, said, 'I can go in and have a look around, but I'd rather know what is going on first.'

I agree. I'm not sure why, I just do. Wholeheartedly.

There are several ways of discovering where damage might be, including the MRI scanner, but the real proof is to find out where the nerves are being squeezed so that the surgeon can then free them in an operation. This involves a technique which I suppose is broadly similar to putting a closed-circuit television camera down the drains to find where your child's teddy bear has come to rest, with the result that ... on second thoughts, it's not quite so similar after all. The tests concerned are known as the EMG and Evoked Potential Test. EMG stands for Electromyelogram ... I think.

We arrived in the Neurophysiology Department, which appeared to be deep in the bowels of a city hospital. Mrs Dudgeon and I, not for the first time, were both struck by how cramped and shabby the conditions were. The staff were all as pleasant as ever, but one felt that somehow they would all have benefited from some decent furniture, a lick of paint on the walls and a cheerier place to work.

I was shown to a room which did have a window, and outside there was a massive building site where cranes swung buckets of concrete back and forth and men hung from scaffolding, shouting noisily right beside the wards where, presumably, lots of people were doing their best to get well.

The EMG test is fascinating. First, one sits in a very comfortable reclining chair and takes one's shoes and socks off. A middle-aged, grey-haired technician, who was very pleasant but looked a little prim, stuck an electrical connection to my foot. The other wires went to my head, and in order to ensure a good connection, can you believe this ... the lady sandpapered my scalp. It's true! It is the most unusual thing I have ever had done to me, and I can tell you that, hospital-wise at least, I have had a few. It is apparently vital to 'get down to the live skin'. The aim of the exercise is to put bearable, tiny, sparkling electric shocks into the foot and catch what comes out of the other end. A computer does wonderful tricks with the information and shows where the 'blockages' are. It's all very simple, unless builders happen to be working outside using a very large electric drill. After an hour the tests were all declared invalid owing to the interference, and we went off to lunch with the promise that someone was going to send the boys round to sort out the man with the drill and play would then recommence at one forty-five.

One of the extraordinary things about the EMG is that it is so sensitive that a skilled neurologist can even tell if you are smiling or not. One has to be incredibly still, otherwise the electrical patterns run amok. Several times I smiled and was asked to relax my face. The only way I could achieve that sort of stillness was to snooze, which I did with well-practised success. Things were less straightforward after lunch, despite the new drill-proof room on a different side of the building, and I am afraid it was all my fault. To be quite honest, it was Mrs Dudgeon's fault.

Whilst at lunch, I told her about being asked not to smile, and she tried to cheer me up with a slightly smutty wisecrack, the gist of which was to wonder if other bodily stirrings might be detectable as well. We both laughed at this and agreed it would be most embarrassing if such things could be detected on the computer screen. I forgot all about it until the very second when the technician said, 'Very still now, Mr Dudgeon. It should be much easier without the drill,' and then of course ... I remembered.

Now, trying not to laugh when you have thought of something funny is rather like trying to stifle hiccups by not hiccuping. One can concentrate for all one is worth and then, at the last moment, it comes anyway. So it was with Mrs Dudgeon's joke. I lay on the couch, desperately trying to think about anything, anything other than the prim and proper operator who might suddenly say, 'Mr Dudgeon! Are you ... please stop it. You're sending my potentials all over the place.'

Of course every distraction I thought of led back to thinking about what Mrs D refers to in our more intimate moments as 'tight trousers'. I distracted myself thinking about her eating her lunch and then remembered that she had had Cumberland sausage. That didn't work at all. In the end my twitching face began to succumb to the smile which crept around my lips, and no matter how hard I tried, I couldn't keep it in. I tried. Goodness knows how hard I tried, but eventually my cheeks billowed out under super-compression and I suddenly burst out laughing. Not a quiet, smirking laugh, which I might have concealed, but a loud explosion of laughter.

The lady at the console slapped her hands on her thighs and exclaimed, 'Mr Dudgeon, you've ruined the run. What on earth came over you?'

I felt suitably shamed, decided that an explanation was probably not in order and apologised like a little boy who has broken wind in front of Great Aunt Mary at Sunday tea. I lay there for the remainder of the tests without even twitching an eyebrow.

Part two of the tests was an altogether more upbeat affair. Conducted by the consultant himself, an enthusiastic man who quite evidently had a great passion for his work, as might a mole catcher or the man sent by the water authority when a leak under the road is suspected; he had that same sort of spirit of enquiry. It all seemed to be a personal challenge to him to find where the nerve impingement was in my back.

He began with an ominous-looking set of fine needles, which

he proceeded to place in my leg to measure how much electricity was being created by my muscles. It was more or less painless and not unlike the sort of experience one might have at the acupuncturist. He deftly moved them up and down, occasionally exclaiming, 'Oh yes. Look at that,' to his technician, who pressed buttons and organised print-out paper. It was great fun.

His party piece involved doing the task the other way round; that is, sticking needles in and supplying the electricity. Devotees of Frankenstein films will be very familiar with this process, which really does have heavy Transylvanian overtones. When the juice was applied, my limbs involuntarily shot up in the air in a most disconcerting manner. It was an extraordinary feeling, as I was not at all sure where the next spasm would originate, but he was enjoying himself a great deal and continued with his loud exclamations to his colleague.

'Oh my! Did you see that? Sixty-three and a half! Well, well,' and he chuckled away to himself while I threw my legs up in the air at a flick of his fingers on the console. Next to a recent birthday outing at a theme park with eleven children, I can honestly say it was one of the most exciting days I have had for a long time. It was marvellous, and if you ever get the chance to go for Evoked Potential Tests, I would say, 'Go, you won't regret it.' I have indeed wondered whether it might be worth running organised coach trips, such would be the power of the attraction.

At home, in my file of hospital paperwork I have a form, a carbon copy of a statement I had to sign, 'undertaking to pay charges in respect of treatment as a private outpatient.' At the bottom of the form, the consultant neurophysiologist has written two words in his own hurried hand. 'Fucked Potentials' it reads. It is true. I would not lie to you. Mrs Dudgeon and I have laughed about it many times. I just hope it was his slightly careless handwriting rather than a comment on my potentials, whatever they may be. It could, however, have explained a great deal about my situation at the time and with hindsight, would have been a useful, although somewhat inappropriate way to tell my children why their Dad regularly throws his breakfast across the table.

'Fucked potentials, my darlings. Fucked potentials.'

9

Having amassed EMGs, ECGs, MRIs, X-rays, EPs, DGs, DTs, not to mention BILLs, I was sent an appointment to see the 'needle team', a highly specialised group who, by means of various torture techniques, can introduce calming chemicals into the inflamed depths of one's spine. The process, known as an epidural, can be extraordinarily effective, seeming to work in a manner which no one is particularly certain about; but it works, therefore they do it. It is a pragmatic response to a problem. The only difficulty that I have with it is that I don't like it. It's an unpleasant idea and can be unpleasant in reality. Always ask to be sent to sleep during the procedure; it's much better.

Early on in my back treatment several years ago, a similar technique, but with a vicious twist, was used to put some nerves out of action. It's called Radio Denervation and, put crudely, it involves lowering a tiny electrode into the back, finding the right nerve and then cooking it for a short period of time at about the temperature of very hot bathwater. The nerve doesn't appreciate this treatment and refuses to work properly for a long period of time, and if you are fortunate, the pain stops. It doesn't cure the underlying problem but, boy, the relief is immense.

The difficulty with this, as opposed to a straightforward epidural, is that I wasn't allowed to go to sleep, and I have to tell you that it was the nearest I have ever come to real torture. I remember being told very forcibly by the old boy who was Chief Needle Man at the time, that I was to 'lie still', because I was squirming around the table like a skewered snake. It is impossible to stay still under such conditions, but I seem to remember that when the probe was in the right place, evidenced by my increased squirming, a nice nurse squeezed a syringe and I woke up an hour later after a very pleasant sleep. Take my advice and tell them you are a terrible wriggler, and don't be afraid to lay it on really thick. If they want you to be still, they will put you out as soon as they possibly can, and I may tell you that whatever it is that they fed into my arm, it was wonderful!

They tried two ordinary epidurals over the course of a few weeks, but neither helped; the pain continued without a pause, which was very disappointing. When one wakes up, drinks the obligatory cup of tea and is helped to the floor with a steadying hand, one hopes upon hope that it will feel different – but sadly it didn't.

Thus it was that a few weeks later, having survived on painkillers, we met our Mr T again, who had the amassed tests before him on his desk. His view was very straightforward. It was surgery time.

We had all hoped that the tests would provide him with the map co-ordinates he needed, but he was honest and said that he still didn't know exactly what was causing the problem.

'We'll look around and find it. It'll be here, or here, or here, or here. Perhaps here,' he said, pointing to the scan, quoting L4s, L3s and L5s. 'See that shadow there, it could be that. There'll be some extra bone around somewhere.'

Mrs Dudgeon and I could not see anything of note at all, and we came away with the distinct impression that he was going to 'dig the road up and have a look at the wiring'. It is enormously inspiring when one meets a surgeon in whom it is possible to have total confidence, and our man was magic!

10

The busy hospital routinely organised all the pre-admission checks a few days before going in. It saved an extra day in hospital. The apparent purpose of it all was to see if I was fit enough to be savaged by the surgeons.

We arrived at the appointed time, and I was allotted an intelligent, pretty young nurse. I joined a jolly conveyor belt of activity beginning with weighing in and measuring. Once again I discovered that I had shrunk, as I seem to have done steadily for the last few years, at least height-wise; width-wise I seemed to be still developing.

It had been very difficult to get adequate exercise despite all the energy I have expended in routines designed to keep my back in good shape. Each day I used an exercise bike and a mini-trampoline in order to cycle and run. The whole regime took about one and a half hours each day by the time the repeated stretchings and yoga-like movements were complete, but despite this the waistline grew. Nothing compares with a busy day which is spent in constant activity from first thing until last. I investigated other home exercise systems during this time and was staggered to realise what was available, all, I may add, at very inflated prices. There is a whole industry out there dedicated to inventing ways of taking exercise without even leaving the centrally heated comfort of the living room. The most bizarre item I came across in the catalogues was a series of videos taken from a bicycle. The idea is that you place your exercise bike in front of the screen, play the video and pretend that you are cycling through the leafy

47

countryside, when in fact you are not. How extraordinary. I wondered if they might have aerosols of country smells to make the experience complete. It would be possible. One could squirt 'Cow-dunged Farmyard' or 'Silage Pit' into the sterile atmosphere of the sitting room and then, doubtless, buy another gadget from another mail order catalogue to 'remove those stale odours effortlessly at the touch of a switch. Batteries not provided.'

Soon after arrival, I also discovered I had not brought my 'sample' with me so I was directed to a WC and told to put it, that is the bottle, through the little door in the back wall when I had finished. Now one of the effects of the analgesics that I was taking at that time was to make me very forgetful, even in the extreme short term, and so, although I had perched my sample bottle on the shelf in readiness, I began to pee and then only just remembered in time that I was doing a sample and caught the last few drops. Far from being what they politely call 'mid-stream', it was more 'end of the river'. I opened the door, a tiny affair above the cistern with some sort of curious privacy screen on the other side, and put the bottle on the shelf of what was presumably the Pathology Lab.

After a few seconds, a latex-gloved hand appeared and took the bottle.

There was a 'humphing' sound from the other side of the wall.

'Not much here, is there?' it said, in what I think was a female voice.

'Sorry,' I muttered.

'Pardon?'

'I said, sorry. I forgot.'

'Forgot what?'

'To do it,' I said and opened the other door, preparing to flee.

'Have a cup of tea and try again. We can't possibly do our tests on this.'

'Okay. I will. A cup of tea. Right.'

Then I went back to the room and the nurse and, until today, I hadn't realised that I never did go back with another offering.

48

My heavy file sat on the desk in a little room as a procession of nurses and doctors came in, asked questions, made notes and departed. Mrs D and I looked at one another as the same questions were asked several times over.

When did you first injure your back? How many stairs have you got at home? How much alcohol do you drink each week? Bowels regular? and so on until they reached a checklist of diseases: heart murmurs, pneumonia, diabetes, pleurisy, glandular fever, leprosy, ingrowing toenails; you name it, they wanted to know, and several times over. When I had completed the questionnaires to everybody's satisfaction, a doctor in a white coat came into the room. He mumbled 'hello' to me, told me his name was Justin Green and ignored Mrs D as though she did not exist, then he sat down at the desk and with a sigh opened the file. He appeared tired and was quite unable to make a connection with either of us. He ran his fingers through his dishevelled hair and sighed noisily again. My fingers were hovering on the chess set in my pocket when the doctor spoke.

'Tell me, when did you first injure your back?' and so on. Whatever else one may say about hospitals, there's never a dull moment, is there?

Without wishing to be unkind to the young doctor, who was doubtless doing his level best and had probably never been taught 'bedside manner', there was something not quite co-ordinated about Dr Green. On first entering, he effortlessly threw his stethoscope across the room in an attempt to close the door. He sat down and the door swung open again, so he rose from the desk and in doing so, shot a pile of notes across the floor in his attempt to push the door firmly shut. He sat down again, and after a while he asked me which drugs I was taking. I listed them for him and he wrote them down. One of them was new and clearly quite unknown to him, so he arose and went towards the door.

'Just a minute,' he said, 'I'll have to get a *Pharmacopia*,' and departed, inadvertently taking the X-ray folder with him on the corner of his coat.

Mrs Dudgeon and I were having great difficulty not dissolving in convulsive laughter as this pantomine progressed before us. It was entirely harmless, but a revelation. The man was an affable clown. I wickedly asked Mrs D if she thought he might train as a surgeon, and we were both stifling laughter as the door opened again.

He came in, pushed the door closed, sat down, then rose to close the door, which had by then swung open again. At that point it became clear that someone outside was used to the door, or possibly Dr Green, for it was pulled closed as if by magic. I was dreading the moment when he would examine me and perhaps forget he was holding my legs in the air and drop them from a great height, but he got halfway through the by-now-familiar checks and seemed to decide it was too much effort, or unnecessary, and returned to his notes. He wrote laboriously, breathing noisily through his nose. I would certainly have whipped his adenoids out if I had been his doctor. Finally he rose and asked me when I was due in hospital. When I told him, he scratched his untidy mop of brown hair and announced that he would probably be looking after me on the ward. As you can imagine, Mrs D and I were thrilled at the prospect and said, I hope without too much reservation in our voices, 'Oh, good. That will be nice.'

He collected his files, his heavy pharmaceutical tome and made a move as if to shake hands with us, but the complex co-ordination required to swap his load from one hand to the other defeated him and he threw the whole lot across the floor. Mumbling and grinning sheepishly, he gathered them all up, collided with the door on the way out, and that, I am relieved to say, was the last we ever saw of Dr Green.

11

When you fix a date for going into hospital it always seems to be an age away, but there comes a time when you have to pull the suitcase from under the bed, dust it, and begin to think about what might be needed for the stay. It's not possible to guess, and actually it's not very critical, as your family will delight in bringing in all the things you never thought you would need. It's not always easy to do this, though, and it can lead to long and convoluted phone conversations while one's spouse searches the places where you last remember seeing the working pair of nail clippers, or that particularly funny late-night play you recorded on tape.

'You could try the second drawer down in my desk, where I keep all the pens. No? Well, look in the little cupboard by the dog's basket. There's a tin in there...' and so on.

Going into hospital produces angst-ridden times of domestic review; should that comfortable pair of old slippers finally be discarded after twenty-three years of loyal service, or should they be retained, despite the fact that every time one traverses the living room, yet another swathe of bits of black flock-stuff falls out of the lining? These are big decisions on a par with buying and selling houses, divorce and all the other crises which are listed as times of major trauma. I'm afraid I played safe and put the dog-eared slippers in a bag in the bottom of the wardrobe and bought some new ones ... super-comfort, wool-lined ones made of elk. They are 'the business', and I have since lived in them by day and even slept in them when putting a pair of socks on in the middle of the night has been a contortion beyond my frail abilities.

Toothbrushes, flannels, pyjamas and dressing gowns all require the same scrutiny. When did I last wash this dressing gown, I wondered as it hovered above my case and, on the basis that I couldn't remember, I washed it. Mrs D asked why I had bothered, as she had washed it last week, just as she had done every week or so for the last twenty-two years. She is wonderful.

I was fortunate in that I have been in and out of the hospital during the last five or six years to such an extent that we actually know the staff quite well. It also meant that I had a pretty shrewd idea about suitable clothes following surgery on the spine. Without doubt, the message here is go for loose ones. Sleeves which do not allow the blood pressure cuff to go around the upper arm mean that every few hours one has to undress, and if after an operation one is feeling sorry for oneself and it is an effort to bend even one's little finger, undressing will not be a favourite pastime. I've also realised that comfort and practicality are everything. Go in in a track suit, wear it night and day and, finally, go home in it. Nobody will care what you are wearing. It also provides ample opportunities for wearing all those T-shirts you have never found quite the right moment for. I have one with a cartoon which depicts a patient standing before the doctor's desk, the man clearly having had most of his legs removed. His trousers drape uselessly across the floor and the caption reads:

'Well, you asked me for an operation to make your willy touch the floor.'

My very dear children gave it to me, and it always gets a good laugh. Aren't they sweet?

Before going to hospital I considered purchasing a personal stereo, and the moment I mentioned it to Mrs D she immediately encouraged me, thinking it would cheer me up. What an angel.

She offered to go and buy one for me, as I was not in my most mobile and balletic state, so before she left I researched the item in a number of catalogues. Our criteria were straightforward: it should have a good radio, and play classical tapes in a way which bears at least some resemblance to the original music. Simple. Unfortunately, our basic requirements test these little machines to their limits. The cacophony of noises my children listen to seem to make few demands on the electronic components and, dare I say it, the children seem quite used to this distortion of sound. Perhaps it improves their music, I really don't know.

I thought I was being helpful when, just before she left, I offered her a tape of Bruch's Violin Concerto so that she could ask the salesman in the shop to play it for her. She patted my arm, told me not to worry and said that she was sure she would be able to purchase a reliable one.

'Leave it with me,' she said.

Several hours later, she returned exhausted and flopped down into a chair with a cup of tea. She gave me a small parcel.

'Duncan,' she said, 'you have no idea how many personal stereos there are in the town. There are dozens.' She sighed.

I opened the box, fitted the batteries and slipped the tape in. Then I settled back into my chair, adjusted my earphones and pressed 'Play'.

The slurring wail which emitted from the earpieces brought me bolt upright. It was just recognisable, but it was a close-run thing; it could have been the local tomcat wailing from our neighbour's garage roof. In between the squealing, periods of silence were punctuated by whirring sounds from the motor within. It was a disgrace. We repacked it and I decided that I would go back to the electrical store to return it.

A little later, I introduced myself to a spotty adolescent in the shop Mrs D had visited earlier.

'My wife bought this, and I'm afraid it's very poor. We've tried a tape and it sounds terrible.'

The youth scratched his face and took the stereo from its box. He shook it vigorously, put it to his ear and then banged it on the top of a fridge.

'Try that.'

'I beg your pardon?'

'Try it. Put the tape in and try it.'

I did and passed him the earpieces.

53

'Sounds all right.'

I pointed out that it did not sound all right; it sounded just as it had before. The sound alternately accelerated and slowed down. I said, 'The speed isn't constant. Listen.'

'Wow,' he said, giving me the distinct impression he had made a discovery.

'Look. You may like it, young man, but I don't,' I hissed.

'Nah, it's called wow when it does that; wow and flutter,' he said and reached for a tape from the counter, replaced my tape and started the machine. He listened, jigged a little and passed it to me.

'Sounds okay. It's your tape.'

I began to look intently at him; a long steady stare which would certainly have communicated growing displeasure to my dog.

'I fink your tape's buggered,' he added.

It was clear that he was immune to glares and body language which indicated that his health and well-being might soon be at risk.

I took a breath and explained as patiently as I could that the tape was perfect and that if he cared to play it through the most expensive stereo system in the store he would discover it was not ... 'buggered'.

He did, and the strains of Bruch soared over the background muzak of the store.

'Uh.'

'I would like to change it for another one; if necessary a more expensive model. I just want to be able to enjoy my music. Can you tell the difference between that,' I said, jerking my thumb angrily at the loudspeaker behind me, 'and that?' I added, pointing to the cassette player abandoned on the counter.

He shrugged his shoulders, took some keys from his pocket and opened a large display case.

'We got all these,' he said.

'I'd like one without any gimmicks. I just want it to play decent music so that I can recognise it. What do you recommend?'

54

'There's this one at forty-two ninety-nine with S-XBS. That's pretty good, or this one with anti-roll extra bass; this is similar but it's got extra super bass and DFTs, and then there's this one with variable tape vibration elimination systems; this has advanced automatic AVLS and this one is neat. You can change the colour of the case ... take your pick.'

He sniffed and rubbed the end of his nose with his finger.

I stared at him uncomprehendingly.

'I think I'd just like my money back, please.'

'Sorry. Can't do that. I can give you a credit note which you can ...'

I drew myself up to my full height, which was a risk as back sufferers will know, then spoke to him through gritted teeth.

'Get me the manager, Sonny Jim, before I ...'

I finished before I described how I would give his nose a very sharp tweak between my finger and thumb and then shut his festering, spotty head in the nearby cabinet ...

Having achieved a full refund, I left the store, but not before the youth had repacked the stereo and placed it back in the cabinet. As I walked past him I picked it up, took it out and put it in his hand. I smiled and gently shook my head.

'No,' I said, and walked away.

At the other end of town was a dear old boy who ran a radio and television repair service with his son. I went there and explained what I needed. He nodded.

'We only keep one type,' he informed me and went back into their store room. He emerged with a small box.

'The best battery wireless there is and a very good little player. No frills and very reliable. I've had one for two years, and I wear it when I'm doing the ironing and hoovering.'

'Wireless!' Now the man was talking my language.

He unpacked it, inserted two complimentary batteries, took my tape, made some adjustments and listened.

'Ah, Bruch,' he said, 'lovely.'

He smiled and passed it to me.

The night before I was admitted, we had a great slap-up meal, as the letter stating my arrangements said ominously, 'Nil by mouth after midnight'. Mrs Dudgeon did us proud, and we really did stack in the pies that night. Only the dog moped, having glimpsed a suitcase, which to him meant only one thing... 'Someone's going away'. Dogs have an uncanny sense when it comes to arrivals and departures; they just do know, and ours always positions himself strategically near to the door lest he be forgotten. He must be in complete turmoil on such occasions, for he very visibly hates long journeys in the car and has to be led to the open boot on a lead as he will not willingly get in without such persuasion. The dilemma must be painful; to go or be left behind?

My family all assembled early in the morning in order to wave goodbye as Mrs Dudgeon and I drove off. The moment was tinged with sadness, but beneath it all I think there was a quiet hope that 'Pa' was, at last, going to be put right.

12

We stepped up to the Reception at the hospital, gave my name, and the lady smiled and ticked me off on her list. There is something about that moment, that mark on the list, which seems to seal one's fate. There is no running away after that. No possiblities for making excuses: 'Um, I think I might have a sore throat and a slightly raised temperature this morning. Cough, cough; you see what I mean?'; no escaping from the process which will then run on to its inexorable conclusion.

I had noticed once or twice before that there is a small group of retired men who receive patients and take them to their rooms. They all look the same and remind me of war veterans parading on Armistice Day, although they cannot be, as they are too young. They all dress tidily with a collar and tie and wear dark blue blazers and, curiously, they all seem to limp, which is possibly not the best advert for a hospital which prides itself on a strong record for orthopaedic surgery. I just hoped that they weren't the rejects, retained under some benevolent scheme to support those for whom things didn't quite work out as planned.

The gentleman who stepped up to show us to the ward was dressed just as the others had been. I believe I am right in saying that he didn't have his medals on his blazer front, but he sported a heavy badge pocket emblazoned with impressive amounts of gold thread, a relic presumably from his service days, and yes ... he limped. Poor man, he didn't look at all fit. Mrs Dudgeon and I both felt awkward at his suggestion that he should carry my case, for he looked so frail, but when I pointed out its trolley wheels, he looked relieved and trundled the case down the wide corridor for us.

There is a compulsory ritual which has to be endured each time one goes to the hospital, and it's not unlike the introduction one is given on arrival in a hotel room when the bell-boy is doing everything he possibly can to earn the tip he anticipates will be forthcoming.

'This is the phone. Dial 9 for an outside line. This is the nurse call button. This is the bathroom. This is the window. This is the bathroom door handle. This is the handbasin and these are the taps. This is the wall and another wall is here...'

'Why, thank you so much. I would never have known.'

I mustn't be unkind. The welcome one receives, the smiling cheery faces, the nurses who come and sit on the bed as if to say, 'This isn't really a hospital and we don't plan to do any nasty things to you; pretend you're on holiday,' were all very much appreciated. It wasn't long before Pat (Hello Mr Dudgeon, I'm-Pat-your-named-staff-nurse-can-I-call-you-Duncan) was doing my 'Obs', Kirsty was checking the details on my papers and Doris was bustling in asking if Mrs Dudgeon would like a cup of tea. The latter was particularly thoughtful, but to tell you the truth, I could have wrung Doris' neck for I was gasping for a cup of tea as I was, by then, two large mugs of sweet tea short compared to a normal morning. Worse than that, we were told it was to be a late-afternoon operation, which meant that ... I had hours to wait for sustenance. Most of a day in fact.

At lunchtime I persuaded Mrs Dudgeon to go to the cafeteria for some food, and I lay on my bed nursing my aching back and imagined her as she walked slowly down a heated servery, taking in all the trays of steaming hot, beautifully prepared food. My salivary glands ached at the thought and my senses were so heightened that when she returned and leant over the bed to give me a fond kiss, I sniffed and was able to tell her exactly what she had had for lunch ... lasagne, hot with lashings of cheese, and wait: I sniffed ... fresh minted peas and, oh my goodness, what's this? Hot apple and ginger crumble. The aroma surrounded her, wafted back to the room by some cruel trick.

For a few minutes I thought, Oh, this is all a bit silly. I don't need this operation. I think we could call it a day. Perhaps if we just left quietly, down to the cafeteria ... and then Kirsty reappeared bearing two wrist bands, and that was it. Click. Click. Got you. Now you are an inmate. It's very final.

Given that the room measures about ten feet by eight and has a chest of drawers, a wardrobe and a bed, it's quite difficult to spend six hours deciding where to put two pairs of pyjamas, one pair of socks, a dressing gown, a washbag and, don't forget, the personal stereo. We arranged them a few times and then re-arranged them until they were to our entire satisfaction. It felt good. Home from home almost, until the sister came in with an Operating Theatre Schedule, told us the expected time of 'going down', even though it was actually up, and left two garments on the bed and said, 'You can change for Theatre whenever you like.'

The operating gown is a familiar garment to most people and, yes, if we're honest, we all have to admit to having put one on the wrong way round at least once. The idea is that the opening goes at the back and it is tied once or twice behind the neck. It certainly doesn't do to walk down the corridor and bend down to pick up something from the floor, but it is infinitely better than wearing it the wrong way round and well ... just walking down the corridor. The prize for the 'ugliest garment in the whole world competition' must, however, without any doubt, go to the second of the two items which lay neatly folded on my bed. The Theatre Underpants. Made of tough tissue paper, these one-size-fits-all, and no, don't worry about distinguishing the front from the back because there is no difference undies, are for your conscious modesty only. The moment you are asleep, they whip all your clothes off anyway. Somebody in theatre, unbelievably, is appointed Cutter-Off Of The Underpants. These delectable little numbers must be the most short-lived item of clothing in the world, having a life span of about forty-five minutes before

59

they are snipped off and tossed into the waste bin.

I have to tell you the truth, I waited until Mrs D and I had said our fond farewells before I changed into these splendid garments.

Shortly after I had changed and paraded once or twice before the wardrobe mirror, there was a tap on the door and Mr Thomas, the orthopaedic surgeon, walked in smiling, shook hands and sat on the bed.

'Well, we'll soon have you sorted out. How do you feel? Good, good. You'll be a little uncomfortable afterwards, but I'm sure we're going to get to the heart of your trouble. Any questions about it?'

I put on my best, super-cheerful front and said 'No, no. Just raring to go. Ha ha.'

'See you soon then,' and with that he strode purposefully away as if he had an appointment somewhere.

Not long afterwards, the sounds of approaching footsteps heralded the theatre orderlies, men in green cotton wear who have the power to reduce one to a gibbering, nervous wreck or calm you with their sensitivity and excellent pre-operative manner.

'Hello,' one said in a super-jolly manner. 'I'm Greg, the Theatre Orderly, and this is Phil. Don't know what he does, and he's damned ugly, as you can see for yourself. Ready for the off, then?'

He opened the second door to allow the bed to pass through. Then they re-arranged bedding, introduced layers of scrunchy rubber and a canvas hammock-looking affair beneath the bed sheets and then from a clip board one read while the other checked the wrist bands.

'Dudgeon, Duncan, 16.6.53' as though I was about to be sentenced.

Then with an athletic gusto which made me very glad I was not lying on the bed, he attacked the foot lever, which rocketed the bed up high.

'Okay! Let's go,' one of them said as though he were supervising the can-can at a holiday camp. 'Hop on,' and with that we sailed through the door, Greg at the head and Phil at the foot of the bed.

60

'Did you hear the one about...' and he proceeded to tell jokes until a faint voice called, 'Wait, Mr Dudgeon, wait.'

I couldn't do much about it, but Greg imitated skidding tyres and the bed lurched to a halt as a nurse ran up.

'Before you go,' she said urgently as though I might be departing this world in the next few minutes, 'these have come for you,' and she thrust an enormous bunch of flowers towards me.

'Why thank you,' I said not knowing what to do with them, 'who are they from?'

She rummaged in the bouquet and produced an envelope. I asked her to open it.

'Um, Dorothy and Alfred.'

'Anything else?' I asked.

'It says, "We knew you should have got some help with that boat. Hope all goes well",' she read falteringly.

'How kind,' I said and sank back on my pillow. 'How very kind of them. I don't think I will take them down, up, with me. Perhaps you would put ...'

'Brrrmmm and off we go! Mustn't keep them all waiting,' Greg revved from behind my head.

Travelling down hospital corridors and through lifts in the horizontal is a remarkable experience, for one does not usually study the ceiling, adorned as it was with pipes, wires and peeling paint. On the way I decided to tell them an irreverent joke about the Queen Mother and immediately regretted it as they started to laugh uproariously and crashed the bed into a narrow opening.

And then we were there, and everything was spic-and-span with bright lights and doors that opened and shut automatically, and we came to rest beneath some ceiling mounted posters of teddy bears and Muppets. Green masked faces looked down as though we had arrived in the bowels of an alien spaceship.

My two friends saluted solemnly and disappeared and the anaesthetist smiled, said 'Hello' and went into a smooth, well-practised routine.

'If I could just slip this round your arm. That's it. Pump your fist. Hmm. Lovely. Okay. Small prick...'

13

Put two war veterans together and it is inevitable that the war-yarning will begin; put two hospital patients together and it is certain that they will indulge themselves in an orgy of medical reminiscing, until those around listen in quiet, bored disbelief as the accounts of their respective treatments are exaggerated in a subtle attempt to out-do the other.

'That's nothing. You mean they gave you a local anaesthetic before they put it in? Ho Ho. They did mine cold,' with a menacing emphasis on the 'cold'.

'Well, how big was it?'

'About so.'

'Huh. No wonder. A small one. The one they used on me was, I swear it, that big.' Grand gesticulations, and so on.

By chance, Seamus, a friend and colleague, had been hospitalised at very nearly the same time as I had been, he for a hip replacement and me for the removal of a few surplus bits of my back. We hadn't quite coincided. A day or two after I left hospital he was admitted, and we found ourselves repeating the pre-hospital courtesies of cards and well-wishes and the general banter which accompanies that nervous period before 'going-in'.

Then when we emerged, like two doddery old men, we would sit and compare notes.

'Do you remember Theresa?' I would say, 'that's right, the staff nurse. Wow! The size of her. I used to shake like a leaf when she was on duty. The very thought of her walking in with that syringe ... she was so big she had joined two belts together to fit them round her middle.'

And Seamus would say, 'She was lovely! What do you mean "shake like a leaf"? She used to come and sit on my bed and was just so mumsy; why, she even massaged my toes.'

But then Seamus likes his women on the big side. His wife is ... no, on second thoughts, perhaps I should refrain from providing very graphic images of the good lady, for I am immensely vulnerable, not to mention slow, at the moment and his wife is ... shall we just say, quite large. In fact Mrs D and I were talking, only the other day, about how some people would not fit on the raised WC seat which Seamus had brought back from the hospital, and I think I can safely say, without resorting to establishing dimensions, that Mrs Mac would have a little difficulty squeezing herself between the handholds at the sides. I know this to be true for I once enquired of Seamus why the toilet roll holders in his house had all been relocated until they were nearly out of reach.

'Most people,' I said, 'keep their loo paper beside the ... '

He gave me a sharp dig in the ribs, clearly meant to silence me in Mrs M's presence, and later explained in a quiet hiss,

'I didn't take them off. She ... she knocks them off.'

'Knocks them off?' I queried.

'Yes, knocks the buggers off,' he repeated with one hand each side of his swaying behind, 'so I moved them out of harm's way.'

And that's all I am prepared to say about the matter; until, that is, I can run a little faster.

Christmas and New Year brought us into a good deal of contact with Seamus and his wife, contact which we might not normally have expected for, being family-orientated couples, we would usually have been elsewhere. The problem was that neither Seamus nor I could go elsewhere. Bending ourselves into cars was just possible, indeed necessary for the trips to the outpatient department for physiotherapy, but we rapidly reached our sell-by dates if we ventured beyond a journey of a few miles. It was a frustrating time for all of us. Seamus tottered around on two crutches, moving from one carefully chosen chair to another, and I spent my time taking cautious steps, sitting bolt-upright in hard chairs and for long periods, lying down on any reasonably flat surface offered to me.

Weeks before, Mrs D had made up a day-bed in the living room so that I would not have to retire to a bedroom to rest. It was a wonderful invention, arranged inside a large bay picture window where it was possible to look out across the garden. As Christmas approached, she had, with one of the children, draped it with fairy lights in an attempt to make it a little more festive. It became known as 'The Grotto'.

'I'll wash up,' Mrs D would say, 'you go and lie in the Grotto.'

How I appreciated that special place just inside the large area of glass, through which I watched the seasons changing, the snow falling and, occasionally, the deer who visited us and nonchalantly ate our rose bushes only feet from where I lay.

It is difficult to describe the weariness which can take over one's back, despite the willingness of the rest of the body to be active, not that my poor drugged head was as lively as it had once been. Again and again I attempted to do this activity or that, only to hear a small voice from my lumbar region which said, 'Hey! You're not thinking of taking me for a walk, are you? No way. Not today. Just feel this ache,' and sure enough, the soggy feeling in my middle would grow until it was impossible not to lie down in a desperate bid to take the weight from the offended parts. Sometimes one has to overcome that, to refuse to submit and answer back, telling the joints in no uncertain terms that they are going to get exercised whether they like it or not. It was as if my spine had a separate identity of its own and the arguing was a constant feature of daily life.

Exercise is vital, for without it there can be no recovery, and each day I would lie on a firm bed and work through a list of prescribed stretches, jog on a mini-trampoline and cycle the exercise bike. It became a ritual for an hour or so every day, and the fruit of the effort became evident as the voice from the nether regions was gradually driven into submission. It worked! The exercise succeeded! It really did improve things, and each day I found myself accomplishing a little more than

64

I had done the day before. Sometimes, Seamus would join me, pedalling quietly on the biking machine, and we would joke about our progress in the mini-gymnasium.

'Ho! Eleven and a half minutes,' he would say triumphantly from the bike as I swung a can of baked beans over my head and behind my back for the fortieth time and then sank gratefully onto a stool. Even our treasure of a friend, Val, who 'did for us', would join in the banter.

'Where are you off to today?' she would ask with a twinkle as I struggled to perch myself on the seat of the exercise bike. 'Do you think you should put a coat on? It looks like rain,' she would say as she trundled the Hoover through the dining room.

Fortunately for Seamus, he was taking less analgesics than I was, and as a result he was able not only to tolerate his beloved alcohol but imbibe at a level which I suspect helped him to pass the long winter days of his convalescence. I only once tried mixing the two, and the pounding head I suffered for my sin persuaded me that I should leave the red wine well alone. Now I have to tell you, there is something potentially deeply divisive about not being able to drink when those around you are imbibing with gusto. I have never been a great drinker, and although I say it myself, I did well, refusing to be depressed by the inebriated laughter which often surrounded me. Instead I pursued a different course and accidently rediscovered a childhood palate for soft drinks ... especially real ginger beer. Throughout Christmas I sank pints of it and managed to create something of a local shortage when, shortly before Christmas, Mrs D once again emptied the shelf in the local supermarket. 'Mum,' said the indignant little boy, pointing at us, 'look! They're taking all the ginger beer. Look at all those bottles!' I confess I felt very guilty and graciously allowed him to have one of the two dozen in our shopping trolley.

Nothing could compare with the zinging taste of an ice-cold pint of the pale silvery liquid. We tried all sorts of alternatives when the ginger beer stocks ran low ... lemon and lime, lemon and pineapple, pineapple and lime, apple and ginger even, but nothing could compare with the ginger beer. It became a form of addiction and the source of much merriment among the teenage children as they fought over my portion of the wine.

'What are you having, Pa?' they would ask. 'Your ginger beer?' and then, 'I'll drink your Chardonnay. Don't worry about it. It is a hardship, but I'm sure I can cope. No honestly, Pa, I can manage the corkscrew too. You really don't have to worry,' and so on, which reminds me that that is a measure of how fragile I felt. Can you imagine being frightened to pull the cork from a bottle lest the repercussion leaves one gripping one's back and staggering towards the nearest bed? That's how it was for several weeks. I was that sore, and as a result, I was still on the tablets.

It was gradually dawning on me that, despite all the exercise, there was still sometimes the same intense pain running down my leg, not from the small of my back, as it had done before the operation, but apparently from my hip. My back was definitely improving despite its grumbling, niggling aches.

When New Year's Eve arrived we very suddenly found ourselves alone. Mrs D and I surveyed the debris as seemingly large numbers of youngsters, who had used the living room as a meeting place, all departed for the hottest parties in town. Having debated whether we really wanted to spend the evening on our own, and deciding it was what the children would forever call 'too sad', we phoned the Macs.

'Sure, we'd love to pop round,' Seamus replied. 'As you can imagine, we're not going anywhere. We'll put some champagne in the freezer and be round in half an hour.'

Having abstained from drinking for so long, I had promised myself a few glasses of celebratory champagne and had avoided taking many painkillers for twelve hours or so in order not to court the risk of the terrible headache I had experienced before. It was a close-run thing, so Mrs D and I opened the first bottle as much for analgesic purposes as for anything else. By the time a very large shadow appeared, somewhat grotesquely exaggerated by the exterior light, we were one bottle down.

'Hello,' boomed Seamus' wife, as she clasped me to her bosom and then deposited a heavy bag of bottles on a chair.

'Stick it in the fridge, Duncan,' she cried. 'Let's get cracking. Four hours to midnight.'

I glanced in the bag and noted three more bottles, all glistening with condensation.

'Gosh,' I remarked, 'I've already got three chilling.'

She grinned broadly, slapped me soundly on the back and Seamus brought up the rear, moving slowly towards a comfortable-looking wheelchair, where he settled for the evening.

Apart from a brief interlude for some light supper, we sat and drank too much Blanc de Noir and swapped, amongst other things, too many hospital stories for comfort until a few minutes to midnight. By then, no less than five empty bottles stood beside the coffee table. We all sat, eyes a little glazed, staring at the television, which had been allowed for the moments leading up to midnight, and then it was turned off and we flung open the windows to listen to the church bells, fireworks and other festivities in the village organised by those who were determined to celebrate in style. We opened the sixth bottle and toasted each other's health and the incoming year. Seamus and I remarked on our stamina which had allowed us to stay up so late, but decided that enough was enough. We were happy but indescribably weary. Shortly after that, Mrs M decided to borrow the borrowed wheelchair and whisk Seamus home in safety lest he fall over in the dark country lane. We bid our friends goodbye as she made light of the steep slope outside our house, Seamus sporting a large torch and Mrs M sporting ... well, Seamus. We tottered, somewhat the worse for wear, merrily away to bed, another year over and a new one ushered in; one which we quite reasonably thought couldn't possibly be worse than the last.

14

It is an extraordinary notion that human beings live their lives by an arbitrary and irregular calendar and yet, despite this, we all set such store by different dates during the course of the year. None produces a more marked reaction than December 31st and January 1st, with their accompanying celebrations and, more importantly, expectations of change. However irrational it may be, we all associate that day with opportunities for new beginnings: resolutions are made, expectations are raised and unrealistic aspirations are pursued. When the New Year's morning arrives, we are curiously surprised. Why, the world is just the same! The washing up is still there, the dog sheds just as much fur all over the carpets, and Monday morning at the office still feels like ... Monday morning at the office. The hype and the razzmatazz turn hollow, if not sour, and we are disappointed. Nothing has changed except the digits of the date. It is a powerful and strange phenomenon. If Mrs D and I had known quite what the New Year was going to bring, we might not have drunk Seamus' champagne with such optimistic gusto. On reflection, it is as well we didn't have foreknowledge, for I am sure we would have been robbed of the opportunity to share such a special evening with two very dear and generous friends.

It is still a source of puzzlement to us that after that evening, everything went backwards. Mrs Dudgeon and I debated whether the somewhat copious amounts of champagne had acted as some wicked catalyst or whether perhaps it was due to the much longer day I had survived without rest, but New Year's Day signalled a major setback. It was a disappointment of unbelievable proportions, somehow made worse by the illogical expectations that the fresh year could not be anything but positive. For four days after New Year, I cycled, exercised and stood in steaming showers to try to shake off the intense pain which now seemed to envelope my pelvis and leg. Swallowing opiates brought temporary relief but nothing would make it abate and finally, at Mrs D's insistence, I contacted the hospital.

'It's as though I never had the operation,' I said to the sympathetic specialist. 'It's all come back with a real vengeance.'

At the hurriedly arranged appointment, there was much talk of inflammation at the site of the operation which conjured up pictures of a pool of stagnating champagne gathering beneath my wound. I imagined them siphoning off a litre or so of now-still best French wine, but the doctor laughed.

'Much more likely to be that you haven't had enough rest and it's all got a little angry,' he said, rubbing his chin. 'I think we need to calm it down again, get you out of pain and get you moving. Can you come back in?'

'Come back in?' We looked at him in horror. 'You mean back in hospital?'

He nodded.

'How long for?'

'About a week.'

'A week?' we mouthed and our hearts sank. 'When?'

'This afternoon.'

A little later we went through the well-rehearsed routine of packing the case. Pyjamas, tracksuits, T-shirts with slogans (including one acquired at Christmas which read, 'Reassembled By An Orthopaedic Surgeon' with a picture of a bemused man who had one leg facing in one direction while the other faced in the opposite one), personal stereo (still working magnificently), talcum powder, regulation two flannels, watercolours, books, Liquorice Allsorts and ... ginger beer.

This time, the theatre nurse put me right out while they fed a catheter into my back, and I woke up in the ward having little or no recollection of what had happened. A tube led from a mass of sticky tape on my hip to a black box which hung beside the bed looking for all the world like the grown-up brother of my personal stereo. A nurse put her head round the door and enquired after my well-being.

'I feel fine. Absolutely fine. In fact ... I can't feel anything at all.'

'Good. Now don't try to get out of bed without one of us with you. You will feel wobbly until it's adjusted properly.'

'Adjusted properly?'

'The pump,' she said pointing at the black box. 'It's dripping anaesthetic into your back. Too much and your legs will go numb.'

'And too little?' I enquired.

'Then the pain will come back. We'll find the right balance, don't worry.'

When I did swing my legs out of the bed and put my feet on the floor, I became aware of the blissful sensation of near-total pain relief which is impossible to explain unless you have experienced it. After months of discomfort, the absence of pain is indescribable; it is like a vacuum, as though an enemy has died. I felt good. Ecstatic. As though I might be dreaming.

'Wonderful. Now, let's try standing up,' the nurse said and I wobbled to my feet and even made it to the bathroom while the nurse held the black box which was attached to me by six feet of fine polythene tube. Afterwards she told me to rest, which I did, lying on the bed listening to a favourite tape.

I must have snoozed for a while, for I was awoken by a clatter as my personal stereo slid off the bed and onto the floor. I swung my legs around, sat up and reached down to pick it up. The next thing I knew was that my teeth were firmly fixed around the wooden arm of the chair beside my bed as my leg buckled beneath me and I sank in a graceful spiral to the floor. Nothing I could have done would have persuaded my leg to push. It was as though it was made of inert rubber and quite unable to prevent my fall. I had slid forwards and from my new, half-sprawled kneeling position, I raised my head, opened my eyes and surveyed the neat row of teeth marks in the varnished wood.

70

Back on the bed, my confidence shaken, I pressed the nurse-call, and when the figure in blue arrived, I apologised for the damage to the chair and explained what had happened. She looked at me incredulously, stroked the impression of my incisors with her fingers and suggested that the pump was set too high. When the specialist arrived he rubbed his chin again and gave me a detailed description (far more detail than I needed, if I may say so) of how he had struggled to place the catheter next to my spine and that he had used a great deal of local anaesthetic. The result was that my leg was temporarily out of action.

'It's probably gathered around the nerve. Don't worry, it will disperse. Stay in bed for a few hours. We won't charge you for the chair.'

Those of you who have had an epidural, perhaps for childbirth or some other below-the-waist procedure, will know how it feels to have zero feeling in one of your limbs. Some poor souls suffer this permanently as a result of paralysis. It is akin to the feeling one has after a tooth has been filled, when one leaves the dentist with lips and face of rubber. If you have ever tried drinking a cup of coffee in that state, you will understand what it is to have absolutely no control over a part of the body which is normally taken for granted. As you wipe the coffee from your shirt front, you may reflect on how you managed to pour the entire contents of a mug anywhere but into your mouth. An epidural anaesthetic acts in that way. One's body feels like ... rubber.

I heard recently of an elderly lady who had an entire hip replacement carried out under an epidural because she was too frail to be given a normal anaesthetic. She was wide awake throughout, which is, to put it mildly, one of the most horrifying thoughts I have ever entertained. If I tell you that she was offered a set of headphones and a choice of very loud music to drown out the noise of ... wait for it ... the bone saw, you will get the gist of why I find the thought almost too much to contemplate. My respect for this good and brave person knows no bounds, and if I met her, I would bow before her in undying admiration; at least I would if I could bend down that far. I only ask that whatever happens to me in the future, please, please, put me to sleep first and wake me up when it is all finished. Thank you.

After a few days, the benefit of the cocktail dribbling through the tube was very evident, for it was possible to work away at exercises without fear of discomfort. Once I had learned to take the black box with me rather than leave it on the bed and try to walk down the corridor, a mistake which results in recoiling back into the room rather like one of those children's games where the ball is attached to a length of elastic, I began to progress.

On Day One, I and another patient, a lady, both of us fitted with the same apparatus, arrived at the physiotherapy department to be assessed; to have a baseline of our physical mobility established. Then our exercising began and twice a day, each day, we would climb stairs, bob up and down from a chair, cycle on exercise bikes, jog on bouncers and walk the hospital corridors while scrupulous records of our progress were kept. I had often wondered why there were penned marks on the wall of the corridor – and now I knew.

'Right,' said our lovely Welsh physiotherapist, 'let's see how far you can walk up and down in five minutes,' and she clicked her stopwatch. 'Off you go.'

The hieroglyphics were distance markers allowing patients to measure how far they had walked. We did not go far. To begin with, walking was a laboriously difficult affair and muscles groaned and refused to work but, as the days wore on, we became much fitter as our backs became used to smooth action again. I ignored the nagging discomfort which persisted down my thigh, and pounded through the wards, up and down stairs, and across the gardens when the sun shone. At the end of the week, our record cards showed six or seven times the level of achievement we had attained at the beginning.

It was a glorious feeling when the nurses slowly teased the catheter out of my back and took the black box away and, for an hour, I had the freedom to wander around my room

72

unfettered. I constantly found myself looking behind me for the pump. In a week it becomes ingrained that in waking or sleeping one is 'wired up', and to move, even to turn over in the deepest slumber without giving thought to the pump, is to risk becoming hopelessly tangled in the tube. In the middle of one night, I had to call the night nurse and ask her to tell me which way to roll over, for I had wrapped the capillary around myself and in my sleepy state I could not work out which way to move to undo the tangle.

'Okay,' she said kindly, 'one turn towards me. Now, lift your arm. Now one turn the other way,' and so on as she drew the tube out to its full length. It was one of the more bizarre middle-of-the-night happenings.

If you wish to experience this joy for yourself, it is easy to arrange. Ask someone to tape a coil of string to your lower back, attach the other end to a four-pack of lager and live with it for a week – and no, you cannot drink it. I swear there was a law at work all through my attachment; it decreed that whichever side of my room I was on, the box would always be on the other side. It really did happen all the time without exception.

I would set the box on the chair beside the sink and wash and shave, then, crossing to the other side of the bed where there was a small wardrobe, I would reach up for a fresh T-shirt, only to find the pump was swinging perilously on its strap hooked over the back of the chair. I would then walk back around the bed, unhook the box, carry it to the bedside locker beside the wardrobe, put my clean vest on, see my tracksuit bottoms on the chair on the other side of the bed, and so on. It went on for hours although, without doubt, the worst error was to catch the tube on the little bumper wheels strategically placed on the corners of the bed (the ones which are put there to prevent the merry Greg and Phil demolishing the walls of too many corridors), with the result that my movement was suddenly arrested in much the same way as happens in a cat and mouse cartoon, usually accompanied by graphic noises such as 'Doinggggggg!' It felt much the same as I imagine the cat feels when, in full flight, its tail is pinioned to the ground by the massive paw of the local bulldog.

73

Anyway, there I was enjoying the freedom of being discon-nected. It was wonderful, and I imagined Mrs D's face when she would arrive to visit me and see my unfettered, balletic state. However, without wishing to labour the point, dis-appointment was just around the corner for, within an hour or so, the effects of the morphine cocktail wore off. I was walk-ing through the hospital at the time, being greeted cheerily by nurses calling out encouragement at the loss of the box when ... the pain returned.

It didn't slip back again quietly by degrees; there was no subtle warning as it crept up on me; it was nearly instanta-neous. One minute I was walking along full of the joys of spring, then I felt a twinge, and then I was sliding down the wall, barely able to remain upright as lightning flashes of pain ricocheted up and down my leg. Some kind soul rushed up with a commode (being the nearest, close-at-hand approximation to a wheelchair) and parked it underneath me, and I confess that I just sat there in the corridor and wept. The New Year had begun.

15

I am not sure what the collective noun for a group of medics is, but one of them assembled around my bed. There was a great deal of sympathetic chin-scratching, and the general consensus was that although the exercise under anaesthetic had generated much benefit for my back, it had also greatly irritated something around my hip. It was rather like driving a car on a fast and demanding journey while wearing earphones with loud music playing; as the oil in the engine ran out, the screeching and grinding had been inaudible, and so only at the moment of turning off the camouflaging, sweet music had it became apparent that all was not well. Steam and smoke issued from under the bonnet. 'Piston broke', as the old joke goes.

The pain was relieved with a small injection into my hip and everyone felt that the warm water of the hydrotherapy pool could only help to bring relief, so I was taken there and, gingerly, I climbed up the steps and into the pool.

Over the years, I have spent hours in this wonderful treatment room, where a modest swimming pool simmers water at body temperature or above. It is not only the perfect antidote to aches, pains and cramped muscles, but the water is supportive and, once buoyant, one is able to exercise in a manner which would be quite impossible in the gym or on a bed. Limbs more or less float, allowing muscles to be stretched and restored, particularly after surgery. The pool is much in demand, often accommodating a dozen or so individuals all working away, albeit with varying degrees of commitment, through schedules of prescribed exercises: marching on the spot, walking, bicycling, sideways leg raises, leg swings and so on.

That afternoon I walked slowly up and down, nursing my annoying leg. It was a struggle to walk steadily and evenly. I rested against the side for a few moments, and as I did so, I noticed a handwritten notice beside a basket on the floor near the door. The basket contained a towel and the notice said,

'Please Wipe Your Crutch On The Towel
Before You Leave.'

I'm not sure how long the notice had been there, but I looked at it as though I had never seen it before and somehow, in the gloomy and despondent mood that filled my head, it struck me as very, very funny. I put a buoyancy support around my neck and lay back in the water. Then I began to laugh, the sort of laughter which spills up volcanically from one's belly. Heads turned questioningly as I sculled slowly up and down the pool, tears of mirth running down my cheeks. Well, as they say ... I guess you had to be there.

I have to confess that the hydro pool has often been a source of great merriment. There is something about the sight of so many infirm, post-operative patients, most of them much older than me, I have to say, all working away, attempting to repair their bashed-up selves. There are all shapes and sizes, unlike most swimming pools, where the fit and lean strut their stuff like peacocks on display. There it is different. To be there one of the basic requisites is to be weak, not strong, and it seems as though that is one of the factors which creates the very special restorative atmosphere of camaraderie. There is a common purpose: to become well again.

'What've you had done?' an old lady asked me one day as she floated past me, her rubber swimming cap pulled down over her ears so that she could barely hear me.

'Back op,' I replied as I 'bicycled' on my back at the rail, and then as she passed me again,

'I've had my knee replaced. Wish I'd had it done years ago,' and then she was off again, later coming back to tell me that she was seventy-seven in a week's time.

There's something very pleasant about such a matey atmosphere, perhaps born of the one common element ... suffering. Everyone there has been through their own personal refining furnace, some more so than others; a few desperately so. It brought me up very short one day when a young man was carried in on a stretcher-bed and craned into the pool. Assisted by waterborne physiotherapists and surrounded by floats, his therapy was simply to relax in the warmth of the water and try to move his fingers or to evoke a tiny movement in his toes. The lad was about twenty years old and the victim of almost total paralysis after a motorbike accident. I can tell you that the half dozen of us there with him that afternoon stopped feeling so sorry for ourselves and gave grateful thanks in the direction of heaven that all we had to cope with was a series of hips, knees and bad backs. As the old adage goes, 'There's always someone much worse off' ... and there always is, especially there.

There are also the eccentric characters who bring a smile to everyone's lips: Mrs Wangleford, a tall older lady with a booming voice and passion for interrupting everyone's private conversations. Absolutely any cue would do...

'Did I hear you say you have children? I've got children. Three! There's Martha who's twenty-nine and lives in Toronto and is married to an architect and is very clever and makes quilts for Red Indians, and Jemima who is twenty-four and has just graduated with a double, double super-plus First from Cambridge,' and so on in a foghorn of a voice while anyone was foolish enough to meet her eye. We all had to listen; there was no way to avoid it. If the truth be known, most of that wing of the hospital was listening to her. It wasn't only our privacy she invaded, it was our physical space too, as she lunged up and down the pool, long legs bearing flippers which threatened to remove slices from some of the frailer folk in the same way that a bacon-slicer cleaves rashers off the ham.

John Martin, on the other hand, was a quiet, gentle New Zealander with two dodgy knees. He frequently came to walk in the warm, supportive, aqueous environment. He once had me in stitches of smothered laughter when it just happened that the pool fell curiously silent and, by chance, there was no background music playing either. I may have had my eyes shut as I practised sitting down on my imaginary chair, but I suddenly became aware of the silence and looked about me. The only sound that could be heard was the rhythmic splashings of a dozen patients all earnestly going about their business, and then John climbed down the steps. John, who always walked with his hands clasped behind his back in the most unlikely swimming pool posture, began strolling up and down, quietly greeting everyone with a nod and a smile.

'G'day,' he would say, in a voice barely above a whisper, and then walk on a little further. 'G'day,' he repeated and so on until the dear man had greeted everyone present. It suddenly struck me as such an unlikely, almost surreal picture that I had to turn away to hide my laughter lest anyone took offence.

On a few occasions, Seamus was in the pool while I was there, his wiry figure tackling his exercises with gusto. Once, when we paused to speak, submerged up to our chins to keep warm, a lady with an exceptionally large bosom began doing the 'sitting on the chair' exercise at the other end of the pool. We watched in amused silence as the most perfect example of wave amplification took place, for every time her huge bust hit the water, a tidal wave swept down the pool, followed by another and another until the compounded effects caused the water to sweep over the tiled surround and onto the floor.

The day after my pump was removed, Mrs Dudgeon came to take me home just as the specialist came to the ward to see me. He seemed unusually quiet as he surveyed me lying on the bed.

'I think you should go home for a rest. I think you've had enough of us for a while. It's going to be a long haul,' was all he said, somewhat ominously.

16

Mrs D and I took the surgeon at his word and had a break. As breaks go, it had the potential to be ... frankly, quite limited. We browsed brochures of holidays in the sun, even contemplated a trip to Venice, anything to get away from the interminable hospital visits and the house which, lovely as it was, had become something of a prison. The problem was that our envisaged trips away all bore serious flaws such as stairs, aeroplane seats, restaurant seats, hotel beds, carrying luggage, carrying passports and even carrying small change. In addition, the only way to cope physically during this break was to take regular morphine which, however good as an analgesic, is not recommended for dealing well with travel agents, customs, timetables, hotel managers or, in truth, anything more complicated than pouring muesli into a breakfast bowl, and even that had the potential to cause complications.

If I tell you that I would sometimes stare at the teapot, the kettle, the water filter and the tea caddy and be totally confounded by the sheer complexity of making Mrs D an early morning cup of tea, you will understand why she was reluctant to take me abroad, such was the impact of the painkillers. My children would sometimes glimpse my confusion...

'That's it, Dad, put the milk in the mugs. No! The mugs. That's the teapot!' or on another occasion, 'Pa, did I see you put the post straight in the dustbin before you'd opened it? Are you sure that's wise?'

They were always very kind about it and treated me with benevolent good humour. The event they quoted most, as they dashed my hitherto excellent reputation before our friends, had occurred when I was taking morphine in hospital and Mrs Dudgeon had come to visit with one of the girls.

Having greeted them on their arrival, my first question was apparently to ascertain where they had parked the car.

'Have you parked the car tidily in the bathroom?' I enquired, which was met, not surprisingly, with blank faces.

'The bathroom?'

'Yes, the bathroom. They don't like you parking untidily. Make sure it's neatly parked in the bathroom.'

To Mrs D's eternal credit she said simply, 'It's fine, darling; parked neatly between the loo and the shower,' which apparently appeased my concerns, made the nurse smile and all was well.

The point was that to go away, away away as opposed to just away, was far from feasible, but the problem was solved when a friend phoned, having heard of the disappointing results of my last stay in hospital.

'I have a bungalow in Wales,' he said, 'it's just sitting there waiting to be used. I won't be up there until the summer. Use it. I'll send you the key and directions. I don't want payment either; just leave a bottle of Scotch in the pantry if you like,' and that was that. We went to Wales.

Mrs D drove and I slumbered my way up the M4, occasionally giving useful navigational encouragement such as, 'Shouldn't we be aiming for Ipswich, darling?' and, 'I never realised there were so many mountains in Suffolk,' but we got there despite my assistance and eventually pulled up outside an attractive little bungalow. It was delightful and reminded us, not for the first time, that we were fortunate to have so many caring, generous friends.

The house was open when we arrived, and Mrs Jones, the wife of Jones the Milk, as opposed to Jones the Wood, Jones the Railway, and Jones the Family Butcher, was there to greet us. Smoke curled from the chimney and a bright log fire burned in the grate. Although we had shopped on the way, while Mrs Dudgeon kept a firm grip on my sleeve for fear of losing a husband in mid-Wales, Mrs Jones had also filled the fridge. It was a real tonic to arrive to such a welcome; we had both feared that the house would have chilled since Christmas when the family had last stayed. It was warm as toast, the bed was aired and the mattress was like a rock. It was only later that we discovered that our benefactor was a back-sufferer who also liked to sleep flat.

The vista from the windows of the house stretched across the rugged Welsh coastline where a threatening storm gathered at sea, obscuring the horizon and whipping the surf onto the beach in a frenzy of white. It was breathtaking, and we both sat for the remaining hours of daylight, studying the view, drinking copious amounts of tea and warming ourselves beside the crackling logs. The change of scene did us both good and after we had drawn the curtains, we studied a handful of guide books to determine where we might visit if the weather improved and I could manage to walk around.

The incessant rain maintained its beating on the roof for two days, with a few breaks which were occupied with taking the dog for some local walks; what the family would call 'an emptying' as opposed to the more extended 'walk'. On the third day, the sun shone and we set off early to visit Porthmadog, from where one of the famous 'Little Trains of Wales' began its steep ascent into the mountains. We were fortunate, given that it was winter, and found that the trains were running, but not until after lunch so we repaired to the town, such as it was, browsed in the shops and walked the streets bathed in untypical winter sunshine.

There is something very depressing about a holiday resort in winter. Optimistic 'Vacancy' signs hung in bed-and-breakfast windows, coal smoke swept across the rooftops, and we were pleased to find a small café open where we indulged ourselves in two 'all-day breakfasts', an extraordinary concept which foreigners must find very confusing. Does one stay 'all-day', or is the food perhaps prepared at breakfast time and kept until evening? Whichever, it was delicious, and the normal budget sausage was replaced by a local-made variety of Welsh lamb.

I have to confess I am something of a sausage fiend. It's quite simple, I love them. If there are cooked sausages in the fridge, I guarantee I will eat them during the course of an evening, preferably with my fingers. Mrs Dudgeon knows my foibles well, and never expects there to be anything left on the plate by morning. Even the dog seems to know when there are sausages around and will respond more rapidly and anxiously than usual to the sound of the fridge door being opened. Together we have been known to clear a plate of seven or eight sausages, although, of course, the dog always has the lion's share. He is such a greedy boy.

As we drove into the station yard for the second time, the air was split by a mournful and prolonged OO-OO-OORR! OO-OO-OORR! and a plume of smoke, moving slowly into the station, signalled the arrival of the train.

'Two and a dog, please,' I requested through the booking office window. 'Returns please.'

'Where to, boyo?' said the round-faced elderly man behind the glass. He had obviously read the same joke in his Christmas crackers, and he broke into a grin when I replied, 'Back here, o' course.'

Having ascertained that we wished to 'go all the way', an expression which I gather now means something quite different, he punched the tickets and bid us an enjoyable journey.

We walked to the head of the train, where an unusual engine with two front ends was being coupled to the carriages. A less than aromatic smell wafted across to us from the simmering chimney. It didn't smell of coal smoke as a steam train should, and on enquiry we discovered that the locomotives were run on oil. Apparently it is not only cheaper and easier to manage than a coal-fired steam engine, but it has the added benefit that sparks do not incinerate the local countryside, which is what used to happen with regular monotony in the summer-dry woodlands when coal was burned. For years, the railway had managed to keep the local reserve fire brigade in overtime money. The fireman also confided that he caught his backside on less bramble bushes as, in the old days, he had to hang out of the tiny cab when he shovelled coal, such was the size of the narrow-gauge footplate.

Mrs D was overawed by the diminutive size of the carriages;

perhaps the cosy proportions suited her, although I didn't say so, but the most enchanting aspect of it was the service which was offered as buffet assistants sidled and ducked through the narrow, low corridors offering tea and coffee. They chatted happily with the few passengers who were patronising the unusual winter service, probably making the most of the relative calm, for normal schedules cannot leave them with a minute to breathe. In a fascinating conversation with a young lass, it transpired that many of the staff were volunteers and that our own waitress was a would-be actor who was between plays.

When she had moved along the train, Mrs D commented that it must be a special organisation indeed to attract such loyal support and that the reward, their delight at seeing a real steam railway plying its way up and down the valley, was a simple pleasure which few youngsters would settle for. It transpired that huge tasks of work had been accomplished over the years of the railway's history, including rebuilding a whole section of line which the British electricity authorities, in their infinite wisdom, decided to flood in a new hydro-electric scheme. The new track climbs in a spiral, crossing itself as it gains height. It was an amazing feat by a large group called the 'Deviationists', who blasted and hacked their way through rugged, isolated countryside, demonstrating that no railway enthusiast can be thwarted by a mere reservoir. When Mrs D heard what the gangs had been called, she commented that it sounded like a religious sect, and at that precise moment we entered a tunnel with another prolonged OO-OO-OORR-OO-OORR from the front of the train.

Had we known what was in store we might have steadied the dog by holding his collar, but we did not. He leapt vertically in fright from where he had been quietly ensconced beneath the small table, emerged at high speed between the seats, managed to turn through a hundred and eighty degrees on our laps, and in doing so knocked my coffee over a light-coloured jacket. By the time the train emerged we had restrained the hound and Mrs D was applying her best lick to a series of tissues in a vain attempt to remove a dark brown

83

stain. Had the coffee been of the normal British railway stan-
dard, the lack of real coffee would have only left a watery
mark, whereas the railway enthusiasts, knowing how to make
a decent brew, had produced a fine beverage with the staining
properties of creosote. All credit to the train crew, they kindly
took my jacket and attempted to wash the offending mark, but
without success. It was a job for the dry cleaners.

On the return journey, we soothed the dog as the tunnel
approached, and all was well. He has always caused us both
great amusement when he has been on *Hercules*, for when the
narrowboat enters a tunnel, the sudden gloom, even with interior lights glowing, persuades him that it is time for bed. He
promptly curls up in his basket, and when the boat emerges
into summer sunshine he stares at us with a huffy look as if to
say, 'Will you please stop buggering me about.'

We had a wonderful day, despite the cartwheeling dog, and
enjoyed a delightful coastal drive back to the bungalow. By the
time we arrived, I was exhausted and uncomfortable, but the
fresh vistas had been such positive therapy that we both felt
our emotional batteries were recharged. On the way we had
purchased fresh mackerel in a fishing village where the lady
serving spoke such broad Welsh that we totally failed to com-
municate other than by sign language.

'Three!' I emphasised, pointing at the fish on the slab and
holding up three fingers.

'Ohyowanthreeoffmamun's besmackie's then duse you, boy,'
she lilted rapidly, or words to that effect, and I nodded, smiling vigorously. For all I knew she might have been arranging
a removal lorry to take all the furniture from the bungalow.

The fish were delicious, even if Mrs D woke in the early
hours with chronic dyspepsia, prompting a nocturnal search
of the medicine cabinet which, fortunately, was well stocked
with antacids. Judging by the numerous jars and packets of
easy-stir extra-hot curries in the larder, I am not surprised the
family were well prepared for such eventualities.

The next day it was pouring with drizzle again, the sort of
rain which permeates any clothing, regardless of the manufac-
turer's reassurances to the contrary. It was market day in the

nearest town, and we ventured in to see a real sheep and cattle market. The auctioneer, even making allowances for the fact that one can never understand such lively patter, was, I am convinced, taking bids in Welsh, for we could not fathom a single word he said. All around, farmers bought and sold, chewed tobacco and spat on the ground in disgust when the sums reached were pitifully low. It was not a good atmosphere. Despite the language differences, one could sense disillusionment in the air.

We turned towards the shops, for Mrs D had thoughtfully brought my tan jacket in a bag, hoping to find a dry cleaner's. After seeking directions and being once more defeated by the dialect, we found one and placed the garment on the counter. To our surprise the shop asistant spoke with a thick Birmingham accent.

'Cloin or super-cloin?'

'I beg your pardon?'

'I said, cloin or super-cloin?' she repeated irritatedly.

Quick as a flash, Mrs D said, 'Super-clean, please.'

'Ah, super-clean,' I repeated, grasping what the girl had said, and then as an afterthought I added, 'I'd just like it clean, please.'

The girl raised her eyebrows to heaven.

'Which?' she said, putting her hand impatiently on her ample hips, which for some reason made me immediately think of Mrs Mac.

'I'd like it clean, please,' I said firmly and I placed a restraining hand on Mrs Dudgeon's hand. 'Just ... clean.'

'If it's doity yer'd be better having it super-cloined.'

'Do you mean that if I have it cleaned it might be ... dirty afterwards?'

'Aw, no. It might not be so cloin, that's all.'

'What! You mean to tell me that...'

But then it was Mrs D's turn to lay a hand firmly over mine.

'I think dear, we'll go for the super-clean, thank you. There's a coffee stain on the front. Be sure to get it ... super-clean,' and with that she picked up the receipt and we left the shop.

We popped into the off-licence, bought several bottles of

best whisky to leave in the pantry when we departed, and set off for the bungalow. The rain continued to pour, and as we drove back, try as hard as we might, we could not see the tops of the mountains around us. A real gloom had descended and there was nothing to do but light the fire and slump with our books. The next morning was even worse and we were drenched by the time we had packed the car. It is one of the things I have noticed about having a bad back and it is patently very unfair, but somehow I always get wetter than when I am fit, as it is impossible to jog back and forth, and dodge the worst puddles.

The drive back was grim until the moment we saw a sign saying, 'Shropshire', whereupon the sun came out over England and blazed all the way home. It was only when we were on the M4 that Mrs D touched my knee and then put her hand to her mouth.

'Oh no! You know what we didn't do before we left town?'

I looked blankly at her.

'The jacket, Duncan. It's still at the cleaner's.'

If you happen to visit Llanfellgeleu, there is a dry cleaner's on the corner opposite the 'Fighting Cocks'. The receipt number is 00237689. Feel free to collect it ... but do please check the front on the left-hand side where there was a large stain. It should be 'super-clean'.

17

We debated how much more 'break' we should have from hospital, given that I could no longer walk without a stick and that daily survival was based only on the beneficial effects of the painkillers, a scenario we did not wish to prolong. It didn't make sense to delay further whatever treatment was necessary, not least because the effects of the morphine were beginning to depress both of us. It is such a debilitating drug that I was quite unable to focus on any useful activity. Reading, writing and being helpful around the house were often beyond me; never was I so glad of my hard-won personal stereo which provided hours of enjoyment, listening to the wireless.

Each day I would tune into 'Woman's Hour' (never the same since it was moved to its morning slot), the 'Afternoon Play' and various other programmes. I am ashamed to say that I must have fallen asleep during more radio plays than any other listener in Britain. Something about the soporific tones of the radio, my comfortable day-bed in the window and veins lapping with opiates, immediately lulled me to sleep. Without fail I would awake just as a pleasant voice was announcing: 'That was a play by Martin Stompford. It was produced and directed by...', and Mrs D would say with a twinkle in her eye, 'Good play, darling?' and continue with her knitting whilst making gentle jibes about how much I had snored. I always made the mistake of maintaining that I hadn't really been asleep at all, which seemed to cause her great amusement.

'Of course you weren't, dear, you were just dozing, I know.'

I phoned the hospital and made an appointment with Mr

Thomas on the basis that nothing was improving, and after a few days we were once again sitting in the Outpatients' Department.

'Mr Dudgeon, how are you? Hello, Mrs Dudgeon. Please sit down. I gather things aren't too good. What a bugger, eh?'

We discussed the symptoms which remained, and I felt curiously ungrateful, for the man very visibly took it as a personal defeat when he learned what had been happening. I reassured him.

'What you did to my spine has made a huge difference and I have managed to get my back fit again, but my hip...'

'Let's have a look at you. Can you get on the bed? Here are the steps. Don't worry to undress, there's no need.'

Mr T gently took hold of my leg and stretched it, rotated it, said 'Hmm', rotated it some more, watched my face for reaction, said 'Hmm' again and then asked if I wanted to sit or lie down, in a manner which indicated that he had something of significance to impart.

'The thing is,' he said, looking first at Mrs D and then at me in turn, 'you need a new hip. It's worn out. Absolutely classic. Works fine as a straightforward hinge but you can't rotate it, can you?'

Mrs Dudgeon and I looked at each other in silence as the shock sank in.

'At my age? Are you sure?' I said.

He nodded.

'Afraid so. It happens. I did a thirty-five-year-old chap last week, so you're not the youngest, but you are young to have it done. I'd like to organise a few tests first to be sure, but they're almost unnecessary,' and he explained how he thought my back pain had been masking the wear and tear of the hip joint which had been finished off by my marathon with *Hercules* in the dry dock in the summer.

'It would have happened anyway at some point. You didn't cause it. What we need to do now is to give you some quality of life back. I can't promise to do anything more for your back, but we can certainly fix this,' he said, pointing at the offending hip.

The notion of having a hip replacement, an operation we associated more with the elderly, was not news we wished to hear. All I could think of was 'another spell in hospital and another long convalescence'.

The surgeon, who had told me he was exactly my age, was visibly fit and had on previous occasions told me he played rugby, went skiing and enjoyed his work which, as an orthopaedic surgeon ... exercised him. The rigours of grappling with long bone surgery probably kept him in trim anyway. I doubted if he needed to go running every morning; with six or seven hips to dislocate each week, he...

I went hot and cold as I sat listening to discussion about cemented and uncemented hips, the former being more suitable for someone with younger bones...

'Your bones are hard, believe me,' he said, and with a mock mopping of his brow he told how he had chiselled away at my spine in order to remove the offending parts. 'The hip will go in well and last you for a long time.'

'How long?' I asked, realising that at my age it probably would not last my lifetime and would need replacing again before I was in my dotage.

'Fifteen years perhaps, can't tell.'

I did some mental calculations ... forty-six plus fifteen ... sixty-one ... at the most.

We agreed a surgery date a few week's hence, and he outlined the recovery progression from two crutches to one, finishing on a stick before glorious full fitness again.

I nodded dumbly, thoughts of Seamus' mobility after six weeks going through my mind. Seamus was sixty-two! What had I done to deserve this? Silly question. I knew exactly what I had done to end up in this state ... the W-Factor was exacting its price.

Back at the house, we flopped, unable to take it all in, and as our children came and went we told those who were at home, made phone calls to those who were at university and spoke to elderly parents, already overly concerned for my well-being. There is a certain irony about phoning parents aged seventy-something to explain that one needs a hip replacement.

'Well dear, your father's in the garden at the moment. He had the chainsaw out this morning; he's cut two tons of logs for next winter's fires and now he's mowing all the grass, and when he's finished, he says he wants to get the scaffolding tower out and climb up on the chimney to repoint the brickwork... We had a lovely day yesterday practising for the Bikeathon, darling. We did sixteen miles; it was a warm up for the real thing on Saturday. On Monday we're off to tour Cornwall, don't forget, so we'll be away for a fortnight...' and so on.

As you may imagine, my confidence was instantly restored by this conversation. I hobbled out into the garden to survey the weeds, which I am certain were nodding their heads in mockery, if not deliberately growing at twice the normal rate. I thought about *Hercules* moving gently on its mooring, untended and unused. It could be ages before we managed to get to the boat again, as the long drive to its home base had been beyond us and would presumably remain so for several months. Try as hard as I might, I felt swamped by it all. It was as though the glimmer of light at the end of the tunnel had been snuffed out leaving us with darkness again.

Mrs D, despite being visibly moved herself, was a tower of strength and encouragement.

'The spring is coming, Duncan. The sun will be shining when you're convalescing. You'll be able to sit in the garden. Shall we go to the art shop and get you those paints you mentioned that you wanted to buy? Just think, you'll be so fit by the summer. We'll be able to get up to *Hercules* again. Would you like to try to get there before you go into hospital? I am sure we could manage it...' and so on as she poured in encouragement and good cheer.

The gloom didn't last long. Soon I was cracking little jokes with the children about always having wanted to trigger airport security alarms with a metal hip, and suggestions flew back and forth across the supper table as to what we could do with the old one. 'A carved door-stop', said one; 'Walking stick

90

handles', said another; 'Soup' said a third, and the dog licked his lips. We had a jolly time.

I made arrangements to have a bone scan and a hip block, the latter being a conclusive way to ascertain whether my hip was at fault. It required a short visit to my friends in the 'needle-theatre' as we now called the epidural administering team. It wasn't a bundle of fun, but they had now got the measure of just how much sedative to give me, and apart from one point in the procedure when I came to sufficiently to feel the anaesthetic being wormed into my hip joint, it was fine. Once I had woken, I had to walk on my anaesthetised hip.

The specialist walked beside me.

'How does it feel?' he asked as I strode normally down the corridor, and I had to reply that I could feel nothing at all. It was quite unreal. The pain had gone.

'Well,' he murmured, 'that's it then. Quite conclusive. Be encouraged. That's what it will feel like after a hip replacement,' and that wonderful feeling of walking on air stayed with me in my mind for a week or two and was a great boost to our morale. It was unfortunate that the anaesthetised hip didn't stay for as long. Sometimes, we had been told, it can last for a few days, bringing blissful release, and an acquaintance had told me how she had been on a hiking weekend with the masking influence of a hip block in place. Unfortunately it only lasted until we got home, and by the time Mrs D had made a cup of tea, I was leaning heavily on my stick again. But we had glimpsed how it might feel in the future ... and it felt good.

In much the same way as we had had to visit another hospital to have my 'fucked potentials' measured, so I had to go elsewhere for my bone scan. The hospital was busy, the staff stretched, and curiously, the same sort of building programme was impinging heavily upon the already cramped grounds. Having allowed plenty of time to arrive and to make our way slowly to the department concerned, we discovered that a nightmare was in store because it proved absolutely impossible to park the car. It was not a good start.

* * *

Car parking must rank as one of the most stressful activities in life, alongside selling your house, divorce, persuading your teenage children to clear up their bedrooms, receiving telephone sales calls for double-glazing whilst draining a pan of hot pasta at supper time, and trying to understand how the vet manages to charge twenty-seven pounds fifty pence for a bottle of shampoo for the dog.

If one were to count up the hours spent by motorists who slowly circulate the car parks of Britain each day, I have a feeling we would be very shocked by the sums. Suppose there are twenty-three million cars in Britain and that half are used each day and have to seek a parking space and that it takes a conservative three minutes to park; one comes up with an annual figure of about three and a half million hours! Believe it or not, that is one third of a lifetime. The truth, of course, is that it is much, much more. The truth is that each year the equivalent of several pour souls spend the whole year doing nothing but attempting to park their cars. I'm just very glad that I'm not one of them.

Not only are great amounts of time wasted parking the cars, but damaging amounts of stress are induced by the very design of the car park itself. I don't know if it has occurred to you, but the spaces in car parks are guaranteed only to allow you to squeeze out of your car if you are less than ten and a half inches thick, and do not allow at all for people who might not be flexible and who find it difficult to get out of a car at the best of times. The same phenomenon profoundly affects mothers with babies in car seats. I have watched parents with small children as they have struggled between parked cars in order to unstrap children from car seats. It is sometimes impossible, and I have seen them back the car out into the gangway, remove the child and place it in a pushchair, abandon the child, get back into the car, park it and then climb out to retrieve the child, who is, hopefully, still waiting in the buggy. To think we pay planners small fortunes to create this discomfort and mayhem. Income from the car park is everything, so, instead of allowing a few extra inches for each car or setting the spaces out in 'herringbone' style which allows for easy movement in and out of the gangways, these people sit in their offices with experimental car park lines arranged on the floor and have games to discover how they can reduce the space to the most exasperating, absolute minimum.

I promise you that if I ever meet a car park planner, I may well lend him a pair of crutches or sticks and invite him to attempt to get out of my car and, while he has his head and neck squeezed betwixt the car and the door, I solemnly undertake to very firmly shut the door. I'm just very glad that I am not Mrs Mac.

After about ten minutes we found a parking space far from the entrance to the hospital, and I walked slowly to the building in the pouring rain. After another ten minutes, spent looking for nonexistent signs, we found the Department of Nuclear Medicine at the top of several flights of stairs. We knew we had arrived by the yellow and black hazard signs on all the doors. 'Warning' they declared, 'Radioactive Hazard'. The atmosphere induced the feeling that we might be met by staff in space-suits, but of course they were not and, far from it, they were as charming and caring as any other medical staff we had come across. After a short while, I was taken to a room with a very large ceiling-mounted camera of similar proportions to a Transit van, and I lay nervously on the bed beneath it. Then I was injected with the radioactive isotope and they plotted its incandescent course through my body. When they observed that it had diffused through to my hips, I was told to return in three hours for the images to be taken.

'Drink plenty of fluids,' they instructed, 'several pints,' which I began to do immediately in the waiting room, where a water cooler stood for the purpose. Within minutes I needed the WC and was amused to see that one particular small room was labelled with a radioactive warning sign and signed 'For patient use only'. Inside, I discovered that they took the contamination risk seriously, even the waste-paper bin being lined with a bright yellow sack bearing warnings. I didn't hurry, but stood having a patient pee, watching the ensuing stream to see if it glowed fluorescently, but it didn't. Presumably, all of the

... matter deposited in that particular small room is actually radioactive and has to be treated as low-level hazardous waste. Much to my surprise, the leaflet we carried away actually warned against coming into very close contact with babies and young children for the few hours after the injection, which reinforced the idea that I might be able to glow in the dark after all.

I made my incandescent way with Mrs D to the cafeteria, where we munched crispy bacon and salad baguettes and drank several pots of tea before walking around the hospital grounds, admiring the skips of builders' rubbish, cranes, concrete mixers and men with the obligatory bum-cracks showing while they laid bricks. It brought home to us how fortunate we were at our 'own' hospital, where the gardens stretched out over acres and acres and indeed, for me anyway, were part of the therapy, even if one was limited to admiring them from the confines of a hospital bed.

Having satisfied ourselves that there wasn't a blade of grass left alive within the hospital grounds, we made our way back inside with the express purpose of finding a suitable horizontal surface where I could abandon my stick and rest, for I had reached my sell-by date and could not remain vertical any longer. We found a bench where I could stretch out, looking for all the world like a down-and-out, and Mrs D could sit comfortably and finish a few more feet of her knitting.

I must have snoozed, for the two hours passed very quickly and then it was time to return to the room with the big camera where, in no more than three minutes, the photographs were completed and we were on our way home. I have since seen those images and have to admit I was sorely disappointed, for all they showed were thousands of little dots which were quite incomprehensible to the untrained eye. Clearly, I had glowed very well for them, and Mr T was pleased to have them to confirm his diagnosis that my hip was to all intents and purposes, in a manner of speaking, on its last legs.

18

Quite by chance the 'guide' limped his way to a room in a
ward which a month or so before had been Seamus' room. The
view was stunning, looking out as it did upon a long slate roof
which obliterated everything except the highest sky ... oh, and
the top of the air-extraction system from the catering department. However, all was not lost for I noticed that it was just
possible to swivel the television around so that the screen acted
as a mirror and reflected an alternative view, which featured
the tops of some distant pine trees.

Mrs D and I both looked at each other after the kind old gentleman had taken his leave (having completed the obligatory
tour of switches, nurse calls, phone, taps, both hot and cold,
the shower, bath plug, bedside cupboard and the wardrobe),
and our hearts sank. For some extraordinary reason, Seamus
had loved the room, refused to be moved from it and couldn't
understand our dismay for him when we had visited.

'But Seamus, it's ghastly. How can you bear to look at that
roof all day long? Ask to be moved when a room is spare. All
the other rooms, without exception, have stunning views across
the Downs...' but Seamus had smiled and tapped the television zapper and with a wink said, 'I'm going to lie here and
watch the box all day, every day: rugby, cricket and snooker.
I am going to binge on bloody sport...' and then with a nod
in the direction of Mrs Mac's retiring backside, as she carried
some flowers out to be trimmed, he said with an exaggerated
display of glee, 'and she can't do a thing about it.'

And that is what he did. Nearly every time we visited, the
sports channel was on, and when it wasn't, the television was

tuned to soaps or chat shows and all manner of highly unsuitable broadcasts, and Seamus would grin sheepishly and turn the volume down very low, but never did he once attempt to turn it off. It was a revelation, but one which explained his indifference to the view which, for me at least, was like a lifeline.

I think Mrs Dudgeon knew that I would be likely to shrivel up and fade away if deprived of a sense of the out-of-doors. It's just the way my life has always been, at least fifty per cent outside in the fresh air, usually with the dog, come rain or shine. All the other rooms, except Seamus', had large french windows opening onto balconies, an arrangement which dated from the hospital's days as a sanatorium for tubercular patients, and I had already gained a reputation for having those doors or the windows open all day and often at night as well. It was possible to feel as though the bed was nearly in the garden. Nurses would come in from the immensely overheated ward and immediately rub their goose-bumped arms.

'Duncan,' they would cry, 'you must be freezing. It's arctic in here,' but I had noticed after a while some came and took advantage of the coolness which contrasted so fiercely with the other rooms, where patients dessicated until they resembled wizened potato crisps. I have never understood the logic of such heating, particularly where the stifling atmosphere must incubate every obnoxious germ for miles around.

I like fresh air, a source of some annoyance to my teenage children, who, having been brought up with central heating, cringe on a winter's day if the temperature drops below thirty-five degrees inside the house. They shudder and instinctively close doors and windows as though the air flowing in to invigorate their little bodies will somehow poison them. Honestly, they could not react more pointedly if mustard gas were streaming into the house. Having hermetically sealed the room I happen to be sitting in, they creep away to their own bedrooms, where the air is feint yellow with a fug which only teenagers can create after a whole winter with the windows latched and firmly barred shut.

*　　*　　*

96

Anyway, the Sister arrived, greeted us both as warmly as if we were long-lost friends, and told me that the room was only a temporary measure until the following morning, when I would be moved.

'We knew he would want his windows looking onto the garden,' she said, winking at Mrs D. 'I seem to recall he likes his fresh air,' and then, throwing a glance at the two tiny open casements, she shivered, rubbed her bare arms and left.

The next visitor was a nurse from the Blood Donation Bank, which also happens to be responsible for the donation of bones. Normally it's not possible to donate one's bones; doing so would probably signal an immediate list to the left or the right, but we had already agreed that it would give us both great pleasure to know that a chunk of my femur could be used for some worthwhile purpose. The head of the long bone is stored to provide tiny slithers of graft which can then be used to rebuild babies' spines when they are born with infirmities, and we couldn't think of anything more beneficial to do with a couple of pounds of my bone if, of course, it proved to be acceptable. There were reams of paperwork to complete, most of it highly confidential, including one form which was passed to me for ticking and secret sealing without another soul seeing what I had written.

In an attempt to sift out those potential donors whose bones might, for various reasons, not be fit for recycling, I had to answer all sorts of fascinating and highly personal questions, most of them causing a visible blush to rise to my cheeks as I worked away with my Biro in the corner where no one could see my responses:

How many sexual partners have you had in the last three years:

   1   2–5   6–10   11–15   16–20   More than 390

Have you ever been on holiday to any of the following:

   Central Africa   Russia   China   Clapham Common

If the answer to the above is 'yes', did you have sexual intercourse with a person not your regular partner while staying there?

Yes   No   Not sure

Have you had homosexual relations with anyone in the last three years?

Yes   No   Can't remember

Have you had homosexual relations with anyone while staying in Central Africa?

Finally, there was a statement which read very diplomatically: 'If you have answered "Yes" to any of the questions 17–154, you should probably reconsider whether it is appropriate to make a donation of bone.'

As the most exciting place Mrs D and I had visited in recent years was Leighton Buzzard on the Grand Union Canal, and as our proclivities for associating with the local population were confined to a brief visit to the Tesco supermarket, I felt fairly safe to sign the declaration that I believed my bones were essentially uncontaminated and fit to be used for donation. Having completed the paperwork, I was told that a little man in a van would drive from North London especially to collect my bone after the surgeon had ended my long and happy association with it later in the day.

Mr Thomas, the surgeon, came to visit us, and was as reassuring and charming as ever. At one point he pulled from his pocket a large black marker pen, asked me to drop my trousers, checked it was my left hip he was about to assault and then made a very large arrow down the front of my thigh and wrote something unintelligible in the size of writing one normally associates with graffiti under railway bridges.

'We don't want any mistakes, do we?' he twinkled. He explained that he no longer wrote on the surgery site itself as over-litigious patients have been suing surgeons after the ink became incorporated into the wound like some ghastly tattoo.

I suppose it does depend what is written on one's leg but, on balance, I am very grateful that I do not have a large and very permanent arrow pointing up my thigh and into my shorts. It could be the source of unwanted attentions at the swimming pool, not to mention in Central Africa.

Mrs D took her leave, and I dressed for Theatre and waited for Greg and Phil to begin their antics, which would signal another horizontal trip through the bowels of the hospital. They arrived earlier than I had been given to expect, and we duly pulled up outside a deserted Theatre ante-room. A female figure in green pyjamas emerged and I was formally handed over again.

I'm not sure why, but I had an inkling that the organisation wasn't to be quite as smooth as it had been before; no anaesthetist appeared, and the theatre assistant seemed to be slightly ill at ease.

'Come far?' she asked nonchalantly, and when I told her where we had come from, she told me all about a shopping expedition she had once made to our local town in order to buy a pair of shoes. It was absolutely enthralling, but I have to say, it did little to reassure me.

'Are they by any chance running behind?' I asked, wishing I had brought my pocket chess set with me.

'I think they have brought you down rather early, yes,' she said a little uncomfortably. 'They're not quite ... ready yet.'

What happened next nearly defeated me. To be more precise about it, what happened next nearly had me vaulting athletically off the trolley and running away screaming down the hospital corridors, operating gown gaping and flapping in the wind. If you have ever waited outside the dentist and heard the high-speed whine of the drill as you await your turn, you will understand why.

I need to explain to you that a bone saw makes a certain sort of sound. It is quite unmistakeable. It is a sort of hybrid noise somewhere between a dentist's drill and a motorbike, with a little bit of car tyres 'swishing' on the wet road thrown in for good measure. As I lay there, that is what I heard. Not just for a second or two but a prolonged, high-pitched, whining, wet sort of scrunching noise.

I looked at the nurse.

'That's a...' but I couldn't quite get the words out.

I tried again as I stared at her embarrassed face.

'Is that what I think it is?' I asked, making sawing motions across my thigh with my hand.

She nodded, pulled a face and simply said, 'Sorry.'

I know I paled. There is a certain feeling one gets as the colour drains from one's face: palms become sweaty, voice unsteady, and one is overcome by what I can only describe as a 'green feeling'. I did debate leaving, and would have done so but for the fact that she very caringly patted my hand and told me with great authority that they had finished. Perhaps her practised ear had heard something I hadn't. Perhaps she had heard something fall to the floor.

19

There is something very original about waking up with a turkey between your legs. In the last few months I had become used to various pieces of pillow-support or wedges and, surprisingly, I actually became used to sleeping soundly with packing under the legs, or the back, or under the tummy and, most recently, between my knees.

As I came to, however unlikely it may seem, my first conscious thought was that, somehow, a turkey had become entrapped between my feet. It had the same weight, shape and general solidity of a twenty-five-pound family turkey, and what is more, my ankles appeared to be strapped to it. I was quite unable to move from my waist downwards.

My second thought was that when I moved my left arm, it felt as though it had been cruelly wrenched from its socket. My third thought was that, whether arm or leg, I didn't want to move much because I was too sore and I was quite happy to slumber away the effects of the anaesthetist's potions.

There was a cage over my legs which in theory should have left my feet free, but they were not, and what is more they appeared to be wrapped in fluffy slippers. Peer as hard as I might under the bed sheet, I could not fathom the construction which kept my legs unnaturally wide apart and my feet anchored so firmly to the bed. When the nurse came to do the routine observations, I asked her what it was that kept me prisoner, and she flicked back the sheet to reveal a turkey wrapped in a cotton bag.

She laughed. 'A turkey? I've heard it called lots of things but never that, but you're right, it looks remarkably like one.'

Then I slept again and dreamt about the hospital phone being bugged and calling Mrs D to say how badly I was being treated, which brought a posse of fierce-looking nurses to my room, demanding to know what I meant by making such phone calls. I knew for certain that it was bugged for there was a small shiny screw in the end of the handset, undeniable evidence of tampering.

'If that's the way you want to play it,' said the tallest and fiercest, rolling up her sleeves to reveal arms which belonged to Mr T, 'we're going to stuff your turkey,' she said menacingly, and with that, they wheeled in a huge trolley of stuffing, whipped back the end of the bedding and proceeded to ram the turkey full of sausage meat.

I awoke in a sweat, my operating gown twisted to throttling point around my neck, and reached up for the 'monkey grip' above my head. My shoulder gave a vicious jab. What could have happened to it? Gingerly, I lifted my left arm up to the hanging handle with my right hand, and then placed my right hand on the handle as well and tried to stretch my back and generally shift myself to adjust my gown, but the effect of being fixed down at one end by twenty pounds or so of turkey, and hauling on the other end, was not a good idea. In between the two was a fragile site at the top of my leg which gave me a sharp shriek of pain, just to let me know that it did not relish being stretched. I sank back onto my pillows, exhausted. Then I remembered my old friend, the PCA, and found it on the quilt. Ah ha! This was the business, and I clicked it, twice, trickling morphine into my veins and before it took effect, I called Mrs D.

I told her I had woken up and that I was feeling reasonable; as reasonable as one can expect to feel, of course, with the turkey and its accessories strung all over the bed.

'A turkey? Duncan, are you taking morphine again?'

'Dearest love, I promise you there is a turkey strapped to my feet. You will see,' and with that, we bade each other a fond *au revoir* and I returned the phone to its rest ... but wait! What a coincidence! I hadn't noticed before that the phone was identical to the one on my study desk. Same model, same colour and ... hang on a minute! How suspicious. A small shiny screw in the end of the handset where mine doesn't have one ... I thought back over my conversation with Mrs D, trying to recall if I had complained or said anything remotely inflammatory. Then I waited with baited breath for the posse to arrive with a large dish of sausage meat ... none came. Phew.

It's a funny thing, but when I woke from my spine operation, I had the most awful pain in the back of my head. Not a headache but a bruise, a bump in fact, but I had no recollection at all of hitting my head on anything. This time, my shoulder was very sore, almost as painful as my hip, so when the lovely physiotherapist, Megan, came in and had finished checking my toe wiggles and had listened to me having a cough, I asked her. She looked a little uncomfortable.

'I think you get bumped about in Theatre,' she said in hushed tones. 'I didn't like to say so last time, but they must have banged the back of your head as they moved you from the trolley.'

'But why is my shoulder ripped to pieces?' I enquired, rubbing it with my good hand.

'Ah, well, I er ... I'll tell you later. Rest it for now. I'll be back to see you this afternoon. Keep wiggling those toes and flexing your legs. On the hour, every hour. Bye for now,' she said, far too cheerily for my liking, and off she went.

Without doubt, the first few nights were the worst, and for me, the part I had most dreaded was being forced to sleep on my back. Mrs D will tell you that I normally sleep stretched flat out on my front and I never, never snore. Turn me on my back and all hell is let loose. I snore like the proverbial pig. My son inherits the same tendency, only he does sleep on his back and we have to close several doors in between his bedroom and ours; even then the ornaments in our bedroom vibrate in unison with his nocturnal breathing.

Constantly, I awoke at the sound of my own snores. I would drift off and then wake with a 'crowp-crowp' snorting noise in my throat. It was quite impossible not to do it, and later it was to be the cause of potential marital disharmony and strange nocturnal wanderings when I eventually returned home. Thank heavens that I was in a room on my own ... the thought of numerous patients all lying on their backs, snoring in fierce competition, disturbing each others' sleep with bed-rattling crescendoes of nasal turbulence, was too much to contemplate.

Many years ago, I recall being in a large men's medical ward where the young and the old lay side by side. Sound sleep was frustratingly elusive, although the place did have its funnier moments. Across the way in an opposite bed was an elderly gentleman who had once, in his prime, been Speaker of the House of Commons, and oddly enough, I recalled him coming to my own school to award prizes on Speech Day. Needless to say I hadn't won any myself, but queues of spotty, swottish boys lined up at the foot of the steps leading to the stage while the Headmaster, a Mr Pigley, read out a long list of names. Lord H then shook them all by the hand, mumbled congratulatory words about the epic effort involved in rote-learning the *Iliad* backwards and later, he made a speech. I don't recall his words, but that is no reflection on what he may have chosen to say; it is more likely that I was probably in the back row, concentrating on a game of battleships. What I do recall, however, is that as an older man, Lord H would sit up in his hospital bed in the middle of the night and, in stentorian tones, shout, 'Order, Order. Will the Honourable Members please sit down and calm themselves? I repeat, I will not have this behaviour in the House.'

Then he would throw back the bedclothes, remove his shin-length nightgown and walk down the ward without a stitch of clothing on until he was kindly but firmly steered back to his bed and dressed by the ever-patient nurses.

'I know they are badly behaved,' the nurses would concur, 'but we can't have you wandering around the House in the altogether now, can we?'

It certainly made the nights more interesting.

After about three days of flat-on-the-back, trying-to-pee-in-the-bottle boredom and agonising compulsory twice-a-day turning and bed-bathing, I was allowed to sit up on the side of the bed. The gruesome bags which caught the disgusting effluent from my wound were disconnected and the drain tubes were removed, a little procedure I will skate over, in case the reader is about to eat lunch.

It was only when I sat up, still nursing my sore shoulder, that I noticed my left foot. I stared in disbelief for there, on the side of my foot, was a row of what were very clearly purple-green finger marks, as though someone had been tugging ferociously at my foot.

'Well,' Megan said, 'I'm afraid they have to pull quite hard sometimes.'

'Pull quite hard?' I queried, 'What do you mean?'

Megan coughed and spoke secretively again.

'I went to see a hip replacement being done once. It's quite ... I mean your shoulder and your foot, they're ... they're from dislocating your hip. You see they have to pull it apart. Someone clearly hung on your foot and someone hauled on your arm ... sorry Duncan.'

I tucked into my pork chop at lunchtime, reflecting on this latest piece of barbarism. I still couldn't raise the fork to my mouth. No wonder. Presumably, the younger one is the harder they have to pull. It reminded me of the games I used to play with the dog and a piece of rope, the aim being to drag the dog along while he gripped the rope in his teeth accompanied by menacing growling. The reality, of course, was that Fido took me for a very long tour of the garden because it was impossible to pull him along once he dug his heels in. Megan confided that one of the surgeons, not mine I am very pleased to say, if confronted by a large patient, will climb onto the table and work from above, straddling the poor sleeping victim in order to get a good grip. Hmmm. I hope Mrs Mac's hips are in good shape.

After lunch, one of those charming blue-rinse ladies came in to adjust my flowers, change the water in the vases and tell me her life history. While she told me all about her husband, who was 'in rubber' in India, I noticed that she was, not to put too fine a point on it, having difficulty with the flowers. She was all fingers and thumbs, dropping blooms on the floor and scrunching the fragile stems. It was only then that I noticed that she had one thumb missing, which accounted for the lack of dexterity in the flower-arranging department. Imagining that she might have lost it in a tussle with a wildcat or a boa constrictor, I was disappointed to learn that her husband had simply shut it in the car door on the Woolwich Ferry.

The constant flow of characters, most of them very special people, was a great joy, particularly in those few early, bed-bound days. Meeting people from many different walks of life and seeking to get to know something about each of them adds greatly to life's wealthy tapestry, and so when Stan came to fix the radiator, we had a long chat.

All through the long night, the radiator had suffered from some sort of high-pressure indigestion, causing it to gurgle, glollop and sigh for hours on end. Stan, affectionately known to all as 'Stan, Stan the Stoker man' from the days when he shovelled coal into the hospital's heating furnaces, spoke lovingly of his calorifiers, his indirect steaming-heating loops and the impossibility of balancing this run and that run, as though they were all his children. He told me things about the hospital's plumbing system that I would never have guessed in a thousand years, and I came away feeling genuinely privileged to be party to such knowledge. As he left, having bled a seemingly endless amount of very smelly air from the radiator (end-of-the-run, you see), he told me conspiratorially of the days when the operating theatres would send down a trolley-full of paper sacks containing ... well, all the bits they didn't need any more.

'Wouldn't be allowed these days. Bloody Health and Safety,' he said, as he departed my room with a grin and I returned to my cherry cheesecake.

The lady who cleaned the rooms in the ward was, without doubt, the character of all characters. She must have been nearing retirement age when I met her. Vera, as she was called by everyone, had worked at the hospital for years. As a girl she

106

had gone into service and one thing had led to another until she had started cleaning patients' rooms at the age of twenty-five. Every day since then, she had mopped and hoovered and dusted and exchanged friendly words with the ever-changing clientele in the ward where she was ... principal treasure. She was a gem. Always meticulously proper, every day she would tap on the door, peer round at me through thick spectacles and greet me with the same concern and politeness.

'Good morning, Mr Dudgeon. How are you feeling today? Things getting a bit easier, are they? Oh good. Isn't it amazing what they can do these days. I'm just going to change your towels for you,' and so on.

What I discovered after a while was that Vera had seventeen cats and a wicked sense of humour. I had had an inkling of the latter when Phil, the Theatre orderly, had run past her in the corridor one day, called a cheery 'Hello' to her and very nimbly tipped her red vacuum cleaner upside down with his foot. It was clearly an oft-repeated bit of tomfoolery, for Vera called out after him and threatened to 'skin him alive' when she caught him, but added '... when I've finished my fitness training at the gym.'

'That boy,' she said to me, 'what would you do with him?' and then laughed like a drain.

After a while we began to tease each other.

'I hope you haven't made a mess in your room again, Mr Dudgeon. I was wondering if you had been having a party the other day,' and I would reply,

'Certainly have, Vera. I've stuck bubble gum under the mattress and my children have been flicking globs of chewed tissue onto the ceiling, and as for the shower...'

Whereupon she would say, 'Thought so. Can't trust you an inch.'

Towards the end of my stay, the Ward Sister apologised profusely and asked me if I would mind moving rooms again to allow them to have a post-operative patient nearer to the Ward Office. I agreed, but hadn't reckoned on Vera's humour.

Shortly afterwards there was a tap on the door, and Vera walked in, hand on hip, looking most put out.

107

'Now, Mr Dudgeon. I don't mind cleaning your room once a day, but I haven't got time to be doing for you twice you know. Look at the state your room's in,' she said, surveying the immaculate room.

'What have you been doing in here, I ask you? You're a terror, that's for sure,' then she broke into wreathes of smiles and set to, moving my flowers and preparing the room for the new patient.

I couldn't help noticing that Vera wore odd shoes; a trainer and an old plimsoll with the toe hanging out, and when I knew her a little better I asked her why. She laughed and told me about her bad toe, and after she had described it to me I advised her to get it looked at.

'It sounds as though you have an ingrowing nail, Vera. I've had them, and they're nasty things.'

A few days later, she came in beaming and told me she had had it seen to. One of the kind doctors had taken pity on her and removed the nail. I met her later, when I was an outpatient, and enquired after her toe.

'Oh, so much better,' she said. 'Mind you, I didn't like changing the dressings. Ugh, can't stand that sort of thing. Couldn't bear to look at it so I left my glasses off while I did it, then I couldn't see,' and she pealed with laughter at her own silliness.

Her daily presence in our lives brought an added dimension that we all valued, and by the end of my stay Mrs D and I had grown very fond of her. She was a very special lady.

For the second time in my life, I was introduced to a Zimmer frame. The new hip felt surprisingly solid when I stood, although the muscles were far from willing to project that leg forward and walking involved throwing the foot with each pace. Sitting was nigh-on impossible, as the angle formed at the hip was too severe for the newly joined bits, but the predictions about the pain-free hip were true. The operation site itself was unbelievably sore, which restricted movements, but putting weight onto the hip was no longer a source of grinding pain. The first tentative steps in the frame were successful, and by the time my children all trooped out to visit, I was mobile, making exciting trips to the bathroom, the wardrobe, the sink, the bathroom again and, when the sun shone, out onto the balcony. Life had great potential again.

20

It is amazing how one gathers pieces of useless information particularly when one is bored and, even more particularly, when one is bored and in hospital.

Did you know that it is possible, using one of those hand-operated 'grabber' aids, to move five hundred grams of loose Liquorice Allsorts into the box in three and a half minutes? Isn't that amazing? It does, of course, only take two-fifths of a nanosecond to spread them all over the carpet of your room after knocking them off the bed with your crutch, but I had so much fun retrieving them from under the bed and clearing them up. So proficient did I become at handling the gadget that I was able to offer the charming hospital chaplain a garibaldi biscuit courtesy of my little 'grabber'. He was most impressed.

I also worked out that nine and two-fifths return trips along the hospital's main corridor equals one mile of walking. I was so determined to get myself mobile that I spent ages walking through the hospital on my crutches. Quite what the staff who work in that long passageway thought of the patient who passed for the seventh time murmuring, '...five hundred and ninety-five, five hundred and ninety-six, five hundred and ninety-seven', I will never know. Whatever they thought, they only greeted my repeated passing with looks of benevolent good humour.

Among the other pieces of information I gathered, it transpired that there are six hundred and seventy-two stairs in the public areas of the hospital. I calculated that they are equivalent to a pretty fair assault on the dome of St Paul's Cathedral or, if practised daily for a week as I did, it approximates to struggling to the top of Cadair Idris; not that I would wish to attempt the Welsh uplands on crutches, but it does give one a more realistic sense of achievement knowing where one might have been, if.

One of the effects of so much crutch-borne activity is that one's biceps and shoulders grow as if by magic. It really is staggering. Mrs D remarked soon after my return from hospital that my shirts all seemed to be splitting around the shoulders. Standing by the ironing board one day, she held one up and asked, somewhat suspiciously, what I had been doing, as though she might be imagining that I had embarked on a secret course of anabolic steroids.

The exercise routines planned by Megan were designed to strengthen the muscles in the thigh and hip. During surgery, many of them have been cut and then rejoined, so it is crucial to encourage movement as soon as possible. That is what one does, alternating hours of activity with hours of rest. It is exhausting, but standing gripping a shelf, marking time, doing sideways leg lifts, then moving onto the bed for calf and knee exercises, quickly restores some strength. The real improvements happen in hydrotherapy, and every morning just after a full English breakfast, Pete, a delightful Polynesian man with the sunniest smile, came with a wheelchair and took all the hip victims one at a time to the pool. There we would experience not only the effects of a large breakfast but also the wonderful buoyancy which enables one to walk, when walking 'on the land' would be beyond the wildest dreams. Fortunately, the water is not very deep and it is difficult to sink, regardless of how many slices of fried bread one has just consumed.

I have only once seen a near-mishap in the hydro pool, and it occurred just after lunch one day when an elderly lady lost her balance. Despite her firm grip on the rail, she slid gracefully under the water. Two of us who were nearby instinctively forgot our back weaknesses and plunged towards her, bringing her up again just as a very pregnant physiotherapist in full uniform flew over our heads and into the pool. Everyone there was most impressed to see one of the staff make such a high-speed, dramatic entry into the water, and concerns turned to laughter as they both emerged quite unharmed by their adventures. The elderly lady blamed her wobbly, frail legs; personally, I was convinced it was the sponge pudding and custard we had all eaten for lunch.

During one of my previous stays in hospital I had got into trouble during one of my wanderings in search of early-morning, healthy exercise. Regularly, I used to slip in and out of a small door into the gardens, sometimes before breakfast, as I happened to be there during a very fine summer. Each day when the sun shone I would leave by the garden door and walk through the grounds, returning by the main entrance, where the reception staff would chat before I continued back to my room for breakfast. It was all very pleasant.

One misty morning, I set off in my tracksuit and was sauntering slowly through the gardens and, as usual, my gaze was on the ground so that I didn't miss my footing on the rough grass, which was full of rabbit holes. I suddenly became aware that, simultaneously, figures were emerging from the mist in several different directions at once. They were uniformed figures with caps and dark tunics, and all were, without doubt, converging on me. It had all the hallmarks of a carefully managed pincer-movement. Anxiously, I stood still and looked from one to the other and mustered my cheeriest response.

'Morning to you all,' I said, which attracted muted murmurings.

'Now, Sir,' said the first to reach me, 'perhaps you could tell me what you're doing here.'

'Um, I'm walking in the gardens,' I replied, holding my hands away from my sides to demonstrate that I was not concealing a Kalashnikov rifle or a hand-grenade belt.

'Don't get funny with us,' said another, whose nose looked as though it may have known fuller and straighter days.

'I think we should take him into Control, Boris,' said a third.

Boris? Boris! I suddenly realised that this had the makings

of an Eastern-Bloc kidnappping and was tempted to make a break for it. Quite what the other side would want with a somewhat physically decrepit biology teacher from Basildon, I could not imagine, but I had no intention of ending up tied to a dimly lit chair in a cellar on the other side of the Berlin Wall. I thought twice about running ... well, just once in fact. I hadn't been able to run for a year previously and wasn't likely to discover how to do it at such a moment, so instead I stood still.

'Come with us. You can explain what you're doing here when we get to Control.'

'But I'm just a patient taking a walk in the gardens.'

'At seven thirty-three in the morning? Likely story,' said the one with the nose.

'I thought hospital patients belonged in beds,' said Boris, and with that we set off towards the building, his hand loosely holding my arm.

Through the mist, a high-pitched female voice called, 'Have you got him yet?'

'We have,' called the nose, 'we've got 'im. You're quite safe now.'

Quite safe now? Got him? What was going on?

We arrived at reception and Mrs Pickington-Smythe, who had just come on duty, said 'Hello, Mr Dudgeon. Have you been out for your early morning walk? What a lovely...'

Her gaze wandered from my face to the faces of the three men. 'Mr Dudgeon?'

'Mrs P, would you please explain to Boris and his friends here that I am a patient and that ...' and then it occurred to me. My wristbands. Of course! Why hadn't I thought of it before?

'Look,' I exclaimed, 'here's the proof. My wristbands. It says here who I am and even the ward I'm on.'

The one with the nose bent to look.

'Humph,' he said. 'Are these real?' he asked Mrs P-S.

'Real? What are you talking about? This is Mr Dudgeon. He's a patient. He's been in hospital for weeks. What are you doing with him?'

113

'He was ... in the gardens,' said Boris furtively. 'He set the alarms off. Major alert on the first morning. We thought we had an intruder. We didn't...'

Boris looked at Mrs P-S's face. He seemed to wilt a little under her icy gaze.

'You thought what? You thought that perhaps an intruder would break out ... into the gardens?'

'To steal the rhododendrons,' I added, somewhat unnecessarily, with a slight smirk now that I could see Boris's face, subject as it was to Mrs P-S's withering look.

'Gentlemen, let go of Mr Dudgeon's arm and allow him to go back to his breakfast. I think we had better have a little talk. I know it's your first morning, but this is a hospital ... not a prison.'

And with that my adventure ended and I went back to my fried bread, eggs, bacon and sausages. Later in the day, the hospital manager came to explain. It transpired that two events had occurred simultaneously. The first was that, unbeknown to me, a new alarm system had been installed on all entrances, and the previous evening it had been commissioned. The second was that 'Incarceration Security Services' had begun work for the first time that night; the hospital's response to increasing fears about security. The alarm had sounded at seven twenty-seven, and Boris and his friends, anxious to make a good impression and earn a few Brownie points, had initiated a full red alert which set alarms buzzing at each of the nurse stations throughout the hospital. The manager explained that several of the security men had just been transferred from a prison and that perhaps it might be wise if he were to arrange a short initiation meeting for them before the day was out ... just to explain the general ethos of how a hospital functions and how it differed from one of HM institutions. I agreed, and we parted the best of friends. I just thanked my lucky stars that Boris hadn't decided to bring his Rottweiler with him that morning.

I still see Boris and the one with the nose around the hospital today. They always give me a certain sort of look as they pass me. I'm not sure, but I don't think it is a friendly 'We've forgiven you' sort of look ... more 'Just you wait until next time'. As a result, I am a little reserved about opening any external doors before seven-thirty a.m. I am quite content just to admire the gardens from the safety of my balcony.

21

It never ceases to surprise me how hospital visitors reveal their true selves during their brief stays. I once had a visit from a chaplain friend, Freddie Ashe, who had very kindly gone out of his way to come and see me. He was a genuine man and certainly had no particular responsibility for me which would have warranted a visit, so I could only assume that he came motivated by some sort of basic pastoral instinct. As he wasn't known locally for the frequency of his pastoral visits, his appearance was something of a surprise. I wasn't in my room when he arrived, instead I was on a bench in the gym, where I was following my prescribed exercise programme. He put his head around the door and greeted me as I did my twenty-ninth tummy squash.

'Hello Freddie,' I said, surprised, from my disadvantaged horizontal position and immediately put my foot in it by asking him if he had been passing when he called in.

'No, no,' he said, 'I came especially to see you.'

'Really,' I replied and added, 'that's very kind of you to come all this way,' for he had travelled ten miles or so.

'Ah well,' he said, 'I know what it's like to suffer with a bad back.'

'I didn't know you had a problem,' said I and realised my mistake almost as the words were out of my mouth. Something in his eye told me the dear man needed a sympathetic audience, and I was, as it happened, a very captive target.

'Oh yes,' said Freddie, sitting down beside me on the bench, 'didn't I ever tell you?' and for the next three-quarters of an hour, despite the best efforts of Megan and the doctor, I could not get rid of him. He talked and talked about his bad back, his osteopath, his acupuncturist, his chiropracter, his twinges, his cold vestry, his bell-ringing difficulties, how he once got stuck on his knees on the chancel steps and when he was through ... he repeated it all again, just for good measure. It was unbelievable. When I finished in the gym, twice as exhausted as usual, he followed me up the corridor and into the Gents until finally, in a desperate bid to be rid of him, I shook hands, told him that I was already running late for an enema appointment and went into a treatment room where I had no business to be. After a few minutes, I opened the door cautiously, peeped out into the corridor and then, seeing the way was clear, disappeared as fast as I could in the direction of my room. When I passed the physiotherapy reception I heard Megan saying, '...I'm sure it does hurt, Reverend Ashe. Book an appointment and we'll see what we can do. Now when could you come...'

In stark comparison was a dear lady, only an acquaintance, who on hearing I had just had an operation and was in hospital, came to visit, brought a delicious jar of home-made marmalade, stayed four minutes and left me with a warm feeling that the world was not such a bad place to be after all. The contrast was remarkable.

Mrs Mac, of course, came with Seamus but they were almost in the league of family. They came laden with gifts which included a week's supply of dried prunes, a little joke we shared, having both suffered the binding after-effects of morphine. Seamus, four weeks ahead of me hip-wise, was still on two crutches and was tired by the walk to the ward, so he flopped onto my bed and reached for the television remote. It didn't work because my aversion to almost all televison had meant that I had never plugged in the set. He fiddled with it and, after a while, shrugged and gave up. Mrs Mac shook the box of chocolates on my bedside locker, found the soft-centred ones and ate them one by one before starting on my grapes. I looked at her from my comfortable armchair. She was perched on my bed. I was sure my eyes weren't deceiving me; it was

117

sagging slightly. A warning label beneath her stated that the bed was only rated to carry one hundred and eighty kilogrammes. I attempted a rapid calculation, but before I completed it, there was a hiss as the bed's hydraulics gave way and it sank slowly downwards, accompanied by a long, sad sighing sound.

'Seamus,' she squealed leaping up, 'you've broken Duncan's bed. I knew you shouldn't have laid down on it. Get up quickly before anyone finds you.'

Our own children were a delight to see, whenever they could spare the time from studying, partying, nights in the pub, trips to Corfu and sleeping it all off. Unfortunately, as anyone with teenage children will tell you, adolescents are essentially nocturnal creatures if left to their own devices. They rise at about one-thirty p.m., crawl out to the kitchen in a mass of dishevelment and grunts, pour cornflakes in the vicinity of a bowl, use the last pint of milk (most of which is splashed over the newspaper positioned under the bowl as an essential accoutrement to breakfast/lunch), and then go back to bed in order to wake up properly. An hour or two later the process is repeated, this time for toast and the cordless phone, both of which disappear into the land of yellow fug. Having arranged the evening's entertainment, they will emerge at about six forty-five, wander into the kitchen and ask 'Wos for supper?' When told, and asked to lay the table, the boys then scratch their chins and mutter 'Mussgoanavashave' and disappear again. The upshot of all of this is that you will be jolly fortunate to see your adolescent children if you happen to be in hospital. By the time they are ready to leave home to see you, it is too late; visiting hours are over for the day.

When the children did arrive, usually singly with Mrs D, they were a joy. Their Dad's antics on morphine were probably a source of good-humoured pub merriment for them for weeks although, to be fair, the post-surgery period has the capacity to be quite disturbing. The tubes, drips, bags and routines of the ward all seem alien and give the impression that the beloved

118

parent has been taken over. For the patient who is quite used to it all, very little has the potential for fear, but routine blood samples or taking blood pressure are the stuff of hideous nightmares for children.

'Oh my God! What's that thing?'

'What thing, darling?'

'THAT! That thing she's put in your mouth!'

'It's a thermometer, love ... you know, for taking temperatures.'

'Ohmagod. I'd never let them put a thing like that in MY mouth. It's disgusting!' which is an interesting sort of response, given the things they frequently seem to introduce into their own mouths...

The younger children bring beautiful pictures of cuddly teddy bears to adorn the walls with messages such as 'Get well son, Daddy' or 'I hope you are filling better', which the nurses all love to see.

'Ah, bless!' they cry. 'How sweeet. How old is she? Six?'

'Seventeen and a half, actually. She's got a bit of a problem with her spelling.'

One of the great pleasures of having family to visit is that it is acceptable to snooze while they all sit around. I only became aware of this retrospectively when our youngest described the first visit she had made after my back operation.

'You were really funny, Daddy. One minute you were talking to us, then your eyelids drooped and you were snoring your head off. Did you realise we had all gone home when you woke up? We watched *EastEnders* and went. You were so funny, you kept trying to pull your oxygen mask off.'

Conversation with youngsters is no more rewarding in hospital than that which you might expect at home.

'What have you been doing at school today?'

'Not much.'

'Not much?'

'Well, you know, stuff.'

'Stuff?'

'Yeah, stuff 'n that. Just stuff.'

Snoozing during less desirable visiting is of course the best way to terminate an overzealous visitor. It should be used infrequently otherwise, if you are too sleepy, someone may mention it to the staff, who will immediately take away some of your analgesics. The knack of accomplished snoozing is to shuffle around in the bed, look squarely at the person who is speaking and allow the eyelids to droop. Jerk awake with a start and apologise profusely, but then repeat the performance again. It works a treat. Keep the eyes closed until you hear the rustle of coats and bags, and when you are certain that everyone in the room is upright, open your eyes just enough and mutter '... sorry, so tired ... so ti...' and collapse onto the pillow.

Be warned, however. You must allow a reasonable period of time to elapse before you sit up in bed and open your favourite paperback. I once made the mistake of disposing of the visitors and settling down with a good novel when I happened to glance up to see a handbag left on the chair. At that very second, a figure crept nearly silently into the room. It is an excellent way to lose your friends.

22

However miserable one feels, and however incapacitated one is, there is always something positive to be winkled out of a situation, if, that is, one has the wisdom and the strength to look for it. Not only is it usually possible to find someone worse off, frequently much worse off, but there are always blessings to rejoice in, humorous moments to chuckle about and most importantly, looking forwards, things to anticipate with a quiet joy.

I am, for example, looking forward to the day when I can put my own socks on. I have put other people's socks on but not mine ... yet. The changing room at the hydro pool reminds me of that old joke about the six-foot chopsticks ... in hell, the incarcerants struggle desperately to feed themselves, but in heaven, they feed each other with ease. So it is with socks. Even two months after a hip replacement it is impossible to bring one's toes near to one's hand, so hooking socks over the foot is impossible. It is, however, quite easy to bend down and help someone else to dress. To give credit where great credit is due, Mrs D has been brilliant at putting my socks on, trimming my toenails and all manner of other intimate, domestic delights.

In the pool, I frequently saw others with terrible afflictions which made me rejoice in my own crutch-bound fitness and vitality, and daily I gave thanks for such taken-for-granted-attributes as sight, hearing and full and dextrous use of fingers and hands. To sit by my balcony doors, a small table drawn up before me with my watercolours arranged on it, and to paint a stormy sky or the long shadows cast across the gardens in the evening, was to appreciate all the precious gifts I had.

The staff who work on a rehabilitation ward all understand the wisdom of allowing resourceful patients to attempt to do things for themselves, however laboured, and regardless of how clumsily they may be finished. It is the very stuff of recovery.

On one of my first vertical mornings, I recall sitting on my bed, clothes for the day laid out beside me, determined to make a good attempt at dressing. Getting a pair of boxer shorts and a pair of tracksuit bottoms on sounds simple enough, and it is, unless it is more or less impossible to lift one leg off the floor. I commend it to you as an exercise in self-awareness: stand and push your pyjamas to the floor; take a stick or grabber and catch them up from the ground and dispose of them; then hook the clean pair of shorts onto the stick and dangle them before the stubborn foot. First attempts to hook them over the foot will fail, and when you do succeed, you will discover that your leg has, almost certainly, gone into the wrong leg of the shorts, so try again. Eventually you will have the shorts on the correct foot and you can place the good leg in the other leg hole. Now stand and try, with the grabber or a stick, to catch hold of the waist band and pull them upwards. By now you will have an appreciation of not only how difficult such elementary tasks are for the infirm, but also how much time and energy is consumed by such basic struggles.

Seamus told a funny story about dressing himself; it happened in hospital late one afternoon just before Christmas. He was struggling as I have just described and without a great deal of success which was, I think, mainly due to his choice of underpants. (Take my advice, go for big ones, ones with acres of leg holes and some substance so that they can be manipulated with a grabber.) Without wishing to cast aspersions on a good friend's choice of underclothes, Seamus was struggling as a result of his sartorial vanity and, as he struggled, he heard the angelic sound of carol singers progressing slowly through the ward. The advance party arrived at his room just as he had

122

succeeded for the third time in getting his first leg through the wrong leg hole, so he was effectively sitting on the bed in the altogether, except that his ankles were adorned with a pair of pants with the flies facing backwards. (There are two lessons to be learned here; the first is to wear an oversized T-shirt at all times, and the second is to avoid sitting dressing on the same side of the bed as the door ... one never knows who may breeze in during your struggles.)

There was a tap at Seamus' door and a tinsel-clad matron waltzed in, crying, 'Mr MacManus, the carol singers are nearly here. I take it you will want them to come in and sing to you. They are collecting for Cancer Relief. Such a good cause, so do have your wallet to hand.'

She smiled broadly, but appeared to not notice Seamus' state of undress or to heed his protests.

'No,' he exclaimed crossly, 'I'm not dressed. Not yet. Wait.'

'Oh lovely. I knew you would want them to come in. Any special requests?'

'Yes. Tell them to bugger off,' he grunted under his breath (I suspect Ireland had had a bad day on the rugby field). 'I can't get my bloody pants on.'

'*O Little Town of Bethlehem*. Right. I'm sure they can manage that.'

Whereupon, the matron disappeared, leaving the door wide open, only to return seconds later with no less than thirteen blue-rinse ladies who filed in with self-satisfied plumpness and surrounded his bed. Seamus tried desperately in vain to grab the quilt to draw it around his lower regions, but he couldn't reach it, or his crutches, without exposing himself further. He told me that the prospect of walking around the room on his crutches did not, at that moment, appeal greatly, so he reached for the nearest thing with the potential to cover his private parts. Now it doesn't take much imagination to realise that stuffing a pillow in one's groin is a poor replacement for a pair of underpants, but that is what Seamus did as he looked around for a sweat-top which was there but tantalisingly out of reach.

Seamus sat through the less than tuneful rendering, wishing

for nothing more than to be left alone in peace and quiet to finish his dressing.

'Now then, Mr MacManus,' said the Matron as the carol singers warbled their way to a close, 'I'm sure you want to contribute to such a worthy cause.'

'Like hell,' he murmured.

Seamus looked around. Wallet. The wallet was in the bedside locker. The bedside locker was ... on the other side of bed.

'Sod,' he thought as Matron, partially realising his difficulties, said, 'Oh, of course. Silly me. You need your crutches, don't you?' and passed them to Seamus as the assembled company looked on. He swears that by then, there was a good deal of nudging and not a few stifled sniggers from the back row.

'I ... My wallet ... it's ...'

'Now come along. The good ladies have three more wards to visit tonight, perhaps you could decide what you wish to give ...'

Seamus rose from the bed, gripping the pillow as firmly as he could between his thighs and tried to move modestly around the room in a sidestep fashion. I don't think I have ever tried to accomplish such a movement, certainly not in front of thirteen members of the local WI, but he did, only to discover that if he moved his legs, which clearly he needed to do, the pillow did not really stay in place. Finally, in a moment of sheer exasperation, realising that he would never see any of them again, he flung the pillow down and slid around the perimeter of the bed.

'Excuse me, please,' he hissed at a lady with twinset and pearls, and a particularly large mole on her chin.

'Excuse me. May I pass, please,' he had to repeat several times to the assembled throng gathered tightly around his bed as he sidled past, still dragging a pair of underpants from one ankle.

On reaching the other side of the bed, he grabbed the quilt and wrapped it around his waist as one of the back row of elderly do-gooders slumped into the armchair in an apparent faint. Locating his wallet, he opened it to find that Mrs Mac had only left him with a twenty-pound note.

'Bugger it. Um, have you got some change...?' he asked the Matron.

'Oh Mr MacManus, so, so generous of you. The ladies are most grateful for your display ... of generosity,' said the tinsel-laden Matron, snapping the note deftly from his fingers. 'Such a good cause you know. Merry Christmas to you!'

And with that they all bustled out.

The reason for telling this story at such length is to illustrate my point: that one can always find humour in adversity, preferably someone else's.

Recently, Seamus told me the second instalment of the carol-singing story, which took place at a dinner party he and Mrs Mac had been invited to shortly after he came off his crutches. Glancing across the room during pre-dinner drinks, he saw a lady he thought he recognised, but he could not quite place her. He thought nothing more of it until the guests were directed to their places and he found himself looking across the table at the same lady, only this time, she appeared to be winking at him. Just after the assembled company had started on their hors d'oeuvres, he noticed the lady opposite dab her mouth with a napkin and, as she did so, the penny dropped. In a flash, he remembered where he had seen her before or, more significantly ... where she had seen him. He described how, as the realisation sank in, he had felt a hot crimson blush rise from his collar and how, for the rest of the meal, each time his gaze met hers, she would wink and give him a small flicker of a very coy smile. Seamus knew what had caused him to make the connection. On her chin was a very large mole.

23

A day or two before my discharge, a message was sent to the hydro pool that I was to be sent to X-ray before I was wheeled back to my room. The ever-patient Pete, wheeler of chairs, left me at the radiography reception, where I sat, somewhat self-consciously, in my dressing gown with wet hair and waited my turn.

Getting on and off strange beds was not my forté at that time, and I was not looking forward to scrambling onto the X-ray couch. There is a strict form for doing all manner of things, and to make the mistake of, for example, approaching a bed from the wrong side or getting onto the raised loo seat without due thought, is not only to court great discomfort but to risk the wrath of the nurses and physiotherapists who are ever-aware of the dangers of dislocating a newly installed hip.

Hips do dislocate, but it is a rare phenomenon unless one is careless or has the misfortune to fall over, hence the little notice in the pool concerning wet crutches. An old acquaintance of Mrs D's, a man of great height called Tom who had been, amongst other careers, a lumberjack, dislocated his long-since replaced hip while building a greenhouse. He was rushed to hospital in great pain and, to his extreme annoyance, was admitted, put on traction and kept in hospital for nearly two weeks. Afterwards, his hip was fine for several years and then it misbehaved again. Not wishing to spend another long spell in hospital, he dragged himself to his garage where there was a beamed ceiling, pulled a box beneath the joists, climbed up and swung from the ceiling. When he was quite motionless, he allowed himself to drop onto his dislocated hip, which drove the head of the joint back into the socket. It made me squirm inside when I heard the story, but he brushed it off with a shrug of his huge shoulders. As they say, 'Children, don't try this one at home.'

The only time I experienced incredible pain in my new hip happened in my hospital room. I was painting at the time and needed to change my jar of brush water and, without thinking, I strode two paces towards the sink without crutches to carry most of my weight. I screamed out loud, turned green and clung to the sink while the room spun around my head, trying to persuade my brain that it was time to pass out. I didn't do it again.

The X-ray of my hip, ordered by Mr T so he could appraise the job one week on, was effortlessly achieved by a very cunning device. The patient stands on a step with back to a vertical bed and, at the touch of a button, the bed slowly tilts backwards, lifting step and the subject to a horizontal position. It's a very simple solution to a difficult problem and one that would have helped greatly on one or two occasions in the past when Seamus has returned, slightly the worse for wear, from a rugby final.

Since Seamus married Mrs Mac there has never been a difficulty; she has a habit of picking him up by little more than the scruff of his neck and carrying him out to the garden shed to sleep it off with the lawnmower. She told me of the occasion when, after such a match, she had collected him from the railway station and he had passed out in the car on the short journey to their house. Mrs Mac left him in the car for the night, only to be summoned by the milkman ringing the door-bell at five-thirty in the morning.

'What the hell do you want at this hour?' she cried out of the upstairs bedroom window.

'There's a ... a body in your car, missus,' the timid milkman called up to the large shape looming threateningly out of the window.

'That's no body, that's my bloody husband. Leave the

127

bugger where he is,' and with that she slammed the casement closed and went back to bed. Given that it was a dark and chilly January morning, I have the feeling that Seamus was quite lucky to have survived the ordeal.

Mr T came in on his rounds and was very pleased with the X-ray, which I had sneaked a preview of as I carried it back to the ward.

'Blimey,' said Pete, in his inimitable Polynesian accent, 'look at the size of that,' and he was right. The hip replacement looks huge, penetrating as it does way down inside the femur. No wonder it feels heavy inside the hip. It is made of titanium steel, and each ball is apparently hand-polished until it glides in the socket to which it is perfectly matched. It was later that I discovered the cost of the replacement as the bills came flooding in again. We had a guessing game at breakfast one morning, but none of the children imagined it was worth anywhere near its true cost of over two thousand pounds.

'God,' said one of them, 'you're permanently worth mugging.'

Mr T was pleased to discharge me and told me he was keeping his fingers crossed for my back, but added that I shouldn't be disappointed if it all took longer to settle down than usual.

'You've had a lot of work done in there. Back and hip are going to fight with each other for a bit. See you in a month's time,' and off he went, with well-exercised orthopaedic surgeon's muscles rippling beneath his jacket.

By the time I left the ward, I had spent nearly four months there, albeit spread over a few years, and it was with a mixture of great longing to be home and sadness at departing that Mrs D and I left. We had both become great friends with many of the nurses who had been so skilled and caring. We left Vera a card, the nurses a pile of much-deserved chocolates, oh ... and the lead from my personal stereo which was hanging on the wall.

Getting into a car after a hip replacement is, to put it mildly, difficult. Driving is of course off-limits for weeks, and impossible anyway as the leg will not push hard enough to work brake or clutch. The day before I left, one of the physiotherapists had taken me out to her car and demonstrated how to slide in; bottom first as far as possible and then swing the legs in. Neither of us had bargained on my unbendable back so, having accomplished the first part with relative ease, I found I could not swing my legs and head in; either my head was stuck against the roof, or my legs wouldn't go in. For a while I could neither get in nor get out, which caused one of the hospital porters great amusement. He offered to get a mate to lift me out of the sunroof at one point but, after a few minutes, I recouped my energy and managed to climb out again. It was a lesson in how little stamina I had to spare and also a warning to use cars with larger doors.

The escapade in the car park reminded me of something which happened to Mrs Dudgeon and me many years ago while we were on the canals in *Hercules*. As I recall, I was in the engine room at the time, tinkering with the diesel pump, when Mrs D came hot-foot along the towpath, having been to the shop, and cried in an unusually anxious manner, 'Duncan! Do come quickly. There's a lady stuck in her lavatory!'

Naturally, I thought it was a practical joke, but it transpired that Mrs D had been walking along the towpath, enjoying the leafy shade with Fido, when she had happened upon a boat. The hirer was leaning with his face pressed to a window, talking to his anxious wife, who was ... stuck in the boat's loo. The lady was very pregnant and had gone into the tiny compartment, managed to squeeze around the door and had locked it, completed whatever she had to do and then tried to leave. She had turned this way and that, and even tried to sit on the small WC while she reached for the bolt and the door handle, but nothing would work. She could not create enough space to swing the door open. Before long claustrophobia struck and her husband heard her calling for help. He, quite rightly, stayed with her to calm her, talking through a very small opening window, and at that point Mrs D and the dog happened across the unhappy pair.

129

When we arrived, the man was saying, 'Okay, now try to fit your knees under the loo roll holder. That's it, stay sideways and reach for the catch...', but it was clear that his suggestion was neither working nor doing much for his poor wife's emotional state, not to mention her knees. We collected a small bag of tools and it was the job of a minute to remove the window. Nobody could get in or out of it, but it was then possible for the husband and wife to see each other properly, in fact for the man to get his head into the loo compartment and reassure his wife. Having done so, he moved aside and allowed me to have a look at the problem. There is something quite original about meeting someone for the first time when they are stuck fast in a lavatory, but that is how Barby and I met. We shook hands, a curious manoeuvre which involved me putting my head through the opening, saying 'Hello, pleased to meet you, Barby,' then withdrawing and putting my hand through to shake hands, followed by my head again.

It was clear that we would have to remove the door while Ken, for that really was his name, talked to Barby. She sat on the WC while he stroked her hand, and Mrs D and I managed to hold the door open sufficiently to get a small screwdriver to the hinge screws so that within five minutes the door could be lifted out and Barby was released. We all had a cup of tea and I offered to replace the door, but Barby would not hear of it, maintaining that she was not ever going in the compartment again if the door was replaced. Bearing in mind that they were only on the second morning of a week-long cruise, I felt the door might therefore become a barrier to her general well-being and left it as it was. Quite what the hire boat company would think when their boat *Buttercup* was returned without a door on the lavatory, I could only guess. We have not met the couple since, but every Christmas we receive a card from them, signed simply, 'Barby and Ken'. No one else believes us either.

On the way home from the hospital, we remarked to one another about the large number of staff we now knew so well. We were aware of their idiosyncratic ways, their strengths and weaknesses and, in some cases, details about their families and personal struggles. One or two staff, particularly Megan, the physiotherapist, had become very special friends.

Over and over again Mrs D and I were both amazed by her insight into the problems of the body. Her gift seemed to be based on an ability to touch and then instinctively understand what was happening. Often she diagnosed problems before the doctors did, sometimes reassuringly.

'Don't worry,' she would say, 'it's just muscles complaining,' or 'A hot pack will sort that out, don't panic; it's not your joints again.'

Most extraordinary of all were 'Megan's Thumbs'. The amount of pain which can be caused by a back full of muscles in spasm is unbelievable. Once, it brought me to a total standstill when my back was at its worst. Megan would do battle with the muscles, a few at a time each day, day after day, by finding the heart of the irascible blighter and pressing her thumb into it, sometimes for minutes at a time. Under her thumb the muscle would contract fiercely, producing very sharp pain.

'Sorry. Sorry, Duncan, another minute,' she would say as I squirmed in discomfort, and then suddenly the muscle would fade and give up its fight. It was an extraordinary treatment, but every time it worked, its efficacy based upon her knowledge of the musculature and her sense of touch, so keenly tuned to what was happening beneath the skin. 'St Meg' we called her, although she blushed to the roots of her Welsh hair when we referred to her in that way.

A very few staff became known to us for their less-than-empathetic manner, and it was extraordinary that all who were inclined that way seemed to like to work night shifts. On many occasions, I would wake in the night, in pain and unable to sleep. Sometimes I would just need to move, a desperate need to get my stiff joints working, regardless of the time of night. Most of the nurses were superb and knew my my great love of cups of tea in the middle of long and sometimes lonely nights.

'Ha, look who's here,' they would say, glancing up from the

nurses' station at ten past three in the morning. 'Where's your mug, Duncan? Want a cuppa?' and they would carry the full mug back to my room for me, and sometimes, if they had time, they would chat.

I never ceased to be amazed by the diverse interests of the nursing staff, interests which were only revealed when they had time to pause. One staff nurse, it transpired, was an expert in architectural details of late-nineteenth-century buildings. She was passionate about the older parts of the hospital and had made drawings and photos of many parts not open to the public. Her knowledge was startling. On her days off she attended college to learn the craft of upholstery restoration, for her ambition was to become the curator of a major preserved house ... meantime she alternated between the intensive care unit and the orthopaedic ward, where she gave unreservedly of her very considerable skills.

I can only recall one unpleasant middle-of-the-night scrounge-a-cup-of-tea-jaunt, and it happened when I was on crutches during my last stay. I was moving slowly up the corridor towards the kitchen when an officious little nurse, who had earned herself a face like a miserable ferret and achieved notoriety for her equally sharp manner, appeared out of a room on the ward.

'What on earth do you think you're doing?' she chided, looking at my mug. At first I thought she was joking ... but she was not.

'Go back to your room at once,' she hissed.

Clearly, I had threatened to disturb the peace of her night-time vigil when cups of tea were not part of her brief. Her manner was atrocious. All I could think of, back in my room, was how much I longed to be home.

And then we were there.

24

Mrs D had been right. By the time I went home, the mornings were becoming lighter and it was clear that spring was on the way; not that the weather improved, for it rained nonstop for a week.

It was delightful to be back again. The space in the house seemed vast compared to the confines of my room in the hospital, and I enjoyed moving around on my crutches. This time I did not miss the security of the routines; far from it, it was wonderful to be able to relax together, taking advantage of the leave Mrs D had decided to have in order to cope with her man who couldn't yet even put his socks on.

The children were as lively as ever, particularly in the evenings, when Mrs Dudgeon and I would run an informal homework clinic and the children would come and settle in turn beside my day bed or Mrs D's chair with questions such as,

'You know this,' (waving a book).

'No I don't; perhaps I could see the book first, and it would be helpful if I had my glasses.'

'It says here that denitrifying bacteria...'

or, 'This essay on *Middlemarch*. We're supposed to be comparing...' and so on, for we were entering the exam season.

The hound had apparently taken to lying on my day-bed during my absence, and the children had laughed about it and placed a cushion between his knees as was my own habit. They reckoned that spreading himself on the bed was his way of coping with the boss being absent, but even he was pleased that I was back, despite being deposed and sent back to a ground-level basket again. He also seemed to understand that the squeaky metal sticks equalled 'no walks'.

The first night presented a problem because I was still not allowed to sleep in any position but on my back, and after an hour Mrs D was awakened by my furious snoring, so we developed a system of me waking and moving to the day-bed in the early hours, a pattern which lasted for weeks. Waking was never a problem because my back became so stiff that I needed to move anyway, and I would make tea and lie in the window under a warm blanket. The dog was pleased. Mrs D was convinced he was smirking at her in the morning, as if to say, 'He's finally decided to spend his nights with me instead of in that room with you.'

Although I needed to return to the hospital hydro pool every other day, we both felt that, at last, we could put hospitals behind us and begin to concentrate on me being well again in time for the summer. We were optimistic that, this time, everything would settle down as Mr T had said, and eventually reach some sort of equilibrium.

On my second morning at home, Mrs D looked a little concerned, as though something was troubling her, and she asked me to come to the bedroom. There she quietly showed me the cause of her unrest: a small puckered blemish on one of her breasts. Despite not being any sort of expert on such things, it was clear that something was not quite right and, without hesitating for a second, we made an appointment with our family doctor. Within hours he concurred and made an appointment for us to see a specialist. Just to be sure.

We sat at home and looked at each other, both trying to believe that nothing was wrong but, try as hard as we might, a powerful anxiety gnawed away at our insides all through that weekend. Alone, we talked honestly together about all the possibilities from the innocuous to the very serious, and I did my best to reassure Mrs D that whatever the outcome, we would be able to cope well. Our happy marriage was, when all was said and done, our bedrock, and we clung to that, and each other, and I have no intention of making light of the

134

profoundly turbulent feelings we endured before we saw the specialist.

The grey-haired Professor was very kind, and actually he was encouraging. He acknowledged a problem existed but he seemed, on balance, to be thinking about a minor problem and, having taken a small biopsy, which was not very pleasant for Mrs D, he seemed to reinforce that view. Further tests were arranged and we came home.

When cancer has already struck down family members, it is impossible to set aside one's fears or to rationalise them according to the statistics we were quoted by the surgeon. Mrs D said she 'just knew'. A day or two later after the radiographers had been at work to amass detailed reports and the surgeon had completed a more sizeable biopsy, the telephone rang. It was the Professor. I saw Mrs D's face fall as she spoke quietly to him.

'I see,' she said, 'yes. Yes. Do you know how large? I see. Yes, I understand. Tomorrow morning at eight-thirty. Yes, of course we'll be there. Thank you for phoning. Goodbye, Professor.'

And that was that. Mrs D had a breast tumour. It was confirmed. She had ... cancer.

We stood and held each other and rocked gently to and fro, leaning against the kitchen sink where minutes before we had been doing the washing up ... and we wept.

25

The rain slashed down in torrents early the next morning as we threaded through the traffic to our appointment. Almost inevitably, there was a misunderstanding at the reception, as I was still on crutches, and the assistant made the perfectly reasonable assumption that I was the patient rather than Mrs D. For us too, it felt strange. For so long, Mrs D had accompanied me and now, only days after my discharge, here we were at a hospital again, this time for her.

Despite everything we had been through – the endless treatment, the needle theatres, the pain, the drugs, the operations and disappointments – nothing we had endured so far came anywhere near to touching the feelings we had as we sat talking to the Professor on that wet spring morning.

He was gentle in manner but firm in his views.

'We need to operate quite soon and I think you must expect to have the breast removed.'

'Is there much chance that won't be necessary?' Mrs D asked quietly.

'No,' he replied, 'I don't think so. I'm sorry,' and there followed a discussion about where the tumour was and why it would be difficult to save the breast and how reconstruction could be arranged later if required and ... and ... and we came out reeling, despite the Professor's best efforts to reassure.

Our resources for coping were either well-honed or depleted; we weren't sure which. It was, to some extent, an advantage to have had so much hospitalisation in the family, as inevitably

136

much of the fear, particularly of surgery, had been dispelled. On the other hand, we knew we were both desperately tired and needed a break from what seemed to be an unending assault upon us. We couldn't believe it. We just could not believe it. As Mrs D said, 'I think someone somewhere has lost the plot.' Neither could our close friends believe it. We went home and lit a roaring fire and just sat and warmed ourselves and talked.

On a purely practical level, we were also faced with Mrs D needing a great deal of physical support when she returned home from hospital in about ten days time, and I, barely able to make tea and carry it through the house without leaving most of it splurged across the carpet, was not in a position to be very helpful. I was also not allowed to drive. How were we going to cope with hospitals? It was as though we were trying to go into battle but some essential requisites were missing ... like boots and rations. I called Mr T who, as usual, was monumentally humane.

'I'm terribly sorry,' he said. 'How absolutely awful for you both. Gosh, you've had a battering. Driving? Yes, now let me see. Three weeks after the op. Try it. You won't do yourself any harm, but you might not be able to yet. No, no, I understand completely. Be careful, but go ahead and try.'

I tried. I sat in the car and tried to push the clutch and brake and couldn't ... it wasn't so much because of pain, but rather because the muscles were not yet reformed adequately to do the job. I was also still taking serious analgesics which, quite frankly, preclude driving. There was little to do about it except that I began to sit in a chair and pump an imaginary clutch up and down, up and down, forcing the muscles to become used to the movements. I also, without overtly declaring it, began to wean myself off the painkillers.

Knowing that I could not drive may have been the turning point in how we approached it all. In short, we knew we couldn't cope without help. Having acknowledged that to each other, we realised that for once, all the offers of help, all those friends who had said, 'If there's ever anything ... anything at all ...' were now going to be called upon to support us.

Gradually we put plans in place, and the offers of help turned to times and dates in the diary.

At the same time as the practical issues were being solved, we were also working through the emotional ones and, of course, high on our list was meeting the needs, fears and anxieties of six children, all of whom were coping with the news in very different ways. We found ourselves listening to the door opening and closing, trying to guess who was coming home so that we might prepare the right sort of mood and attitude to suit whichever child was joining us. It was not an easy week and, during that time, we were very aware that Mrs D herself needed to conserve her resources.

The balance between taking life seriously and taking it too seriously is always a difficult one, but Mrs D and I share one great strength ... a sense of humour. By contrast, it's also probably fair to say that, when called upon to do so, we are able to plumb the darkest depths together, so there was no lack of realism about our situation. We went to those depths in the week before surgery, shared our worst fears and then came out of it both feeling more secure. When I heard Mrs D saying things like, 'Well, who needs two of them anyway,' and, as she looked in the mirror one evening, 'Do you think they might move some of my backside up to the top?' we knew we had found that greatest gift again; to be able to laugh in the midst of adversity. Having said that, the nature of the trauma is that it is genuinely possible to move from hysterical laughter to tears and then back again, all in the space of time it takes to ask, 'Which nighties should I wear in hospital?'

One of the pleasant things we had never prepared for was the number of people who wrote to us during our times in hospital. We didn't know we had so many friends and people who cared! The children pulled our legs mercilessly about it, making great play by mock-staggering in under the weight of the mail.

'Have you two been sending these to yourselves? You don't have to, you know. We all know you haven't got any friends,' and other such charming little jests. Daily, we were moved to tears by the contents of cards and letters, which was yet more grist to the teenagers' mill for a potential joke. Our living room began to look as though it was Christmas with the card strings, re-strung for the purpose, straining under all the good wishes.

Again, just as friends revealed themselves by the way they tackled hospital visiting, it was interesting to note how, based on what they wrote, people responded to our adversity and, in particular, the big C word. People caricatured themselves in 'get well' cards. Those who had had direct or indirect experience poured out wisdom and encouragement, told stories of loved ones or friends who had had breast cancer and had survived to live healthily and happily ever after. Others wrote sincere, simple words: 'Thinking of you at a difficult time'; 'Our best thoughts are winging their way to you both'; or simply, 'With fond best wishes' from people we hardly knew. On the phone, it was interesting that many times, over the weeks which followed, we were put into the position of having to meet the very personal fears and unresolved grief of others, and not vice versa, as one might expect. It had the potential to be exhausting.

Without doubt, the best phone call we ever received was from an old friend who summed up our feelings entirely when she greeted Mrs D. 'Oh, Bugger!' was all she said.

Mrs D and I remarked to one another how the human mind has an extraordinary capacity to move into a new and frightening situation, assimilate the information and begin to deal with it, so that within the week a whole new fluent vocabulary had entered our home in a way that we would not previously have thought possible. Discussions about mastectomies, chemotherapy, radiotherapy, prostheses, reconstruction and, most importantly, 'having cancer' became commonplace; we had moved on, or perhaps been moved on, at a surprising rate. By the time Mrs D faced her surgery, she was quite level about it all and approached it with a fortitude which, previously, I could only have guessed at.

'If I've got cancer in my breast,' she would say, 'then I want to be rid of it ... let's get it cleared out and have the peace of mind...' and so on.

Dear reader, Mrs D and I hope you never have to cross the bridges we walked across hand in hand that week, but if you do, remember there is no rule book for coping; there are no standards for reacting in a given set of ways – you simply have to go with whatever all of it brings you, and be real. It is a sobering thought that, according to the statistics, many of you will walk the same path at some time in the future.

To the husbands who might one day read this book, I would simply say that your emotional support will probably make all the difference in the world. If you can't cope, then get help and, believe me, there is plenty of it around if you need it. Major breast surgery is very, very common, and there are all sorts of support agencies out there waiting to help you. If you add your own baggage to your wife's difficulties you will, at best, compound her problems and make her journey more difficult and, at worst, you could make it all virtually unmanageable. If you want a framework for sorting out your thinking you can ask yourself this key question: how would I wish my partner to react to me if I were about to lose one, or both, testicles? When you have the answer, you will know how to support your wife. The fact is, if you were lovable before, you will be just as lovable without your bollocks. Possibly much more so.

26

'Well,' said Mrs D as I sat on the edge of the bed, 'I'm pleased to have got that off my chest.' She gave me a wobbly smile, held my hand and tears rolled down both of our cheeks.

Only hours previously I had sat with her during all the pre-surgery checks.

'Might I feel sick after the anaesthetic? I have done once before.'

The nurse reassured her.

'We'll make sure you don't; we'll give you something for it, but it's unusual these days. The worst effect people report is feeling a bit flat.'

'Feeling a bit flat?'

We all looked at each other, our faces breaking into broad smiles.

'I think I might well do,' said Mrs D laughing, and from that moment onwards there was a wonderful rapport between us all in Room 224.

Nobody could have hoped for the great warmth, the empathy or straightforward wealth of kindness which emanated from the staff on Mrs D's ward. Being on two crutches, I became the subject of a good deal of gentle banter, but nothing was too much trouble, and far from feeling that we were caught up in a horrendous nightmare, we felt secure in the special atmosphere they all created. It is a sobering fact, but the frequency with which women of all ages suffer from breast cancer meant that these highly professional women were used

141

to coping with it all. Their daily work held no surprises for them.

Seamus had driven us to the hospital, dropping us and quietly slipping away. Over the following weeks we were to give thanks for such loyal and devoted friends. Something about our parallel course through hospitals had created a special bond, not least because when we didn't feel like seeing anyone, Seamus and Mrs Mac completely understood.

'I could pop round, if you like, or shall I piss off?' he would say.

'Um, piss off. We'll see you tomorrow.'

'Okay. Give the old girl my love,' he would say, 'see you later.'

It was great. Just the way it should be with mates. Sometimes, visitors and friends are not so easy to manage. With the best will in the world, they can be exhausting and just what one doesn't need at such times. The one who dropped in on the eve of Mrs D's op came with a heart of gold and a mass of his own unresolved grief, and collapsed on Mrs D just as she was all buoyed-up to face her own ordeal. I suppose that's what makes the world go around. It's just not a predictable place to live in at times, is it?

When Mrs D had been given her pre-medication and she was dozing peacefully I left, as we had agreed, before the theatre staff came, although things were more sedate in this hospital and I doubted that they owned a turbo-charged trolley, let alone a Greg or a Phil. As I walked slowly out of the hospital to another friend in another car, I understood what Mrs D had said to me so many times before. It's easier to be in the bed than to watch the patient. I would have given anything to have swapped places with my lovely, brave wife.

The four or five hours which elapsed were some of the longest I have ever known. I prepared lunch and sat looking at it with no appetite, and even the hound humphed down on his bed with a look that quite simply said, 'Well, bugger it all.'

When the phone rang much earlier than I expected, I was

surprised to hear a slurred little croaky voice saying, 'It's me. I'm back. It's all over.'

Actually ... it wasn't all over. It was in one sense, but in another it was just the beginning, and when I sat beside Mrs D and she cracked her now-famous joke about 'getting it all off her chest', we both knew we had a long way to go but that we could cope and, for a fair proportion of the time, that we could do it with smiles.

One of the first problems we had to cope with was that within an hour or two the room looked like a stand at the Chelsea Flower Show. The air hung heavily with rich scents and every available space was occupied with the most wonderful bouquets and displays. They were everywhere. They were on the cupboards, the window sill, shelves, on the floor and even in the bathroom. One arrangement was so heavy that I could not even pick the basket up, not that that was much of an indication of anything at all as I was still having serious trouble filling a kettle. We were overwhelmed by the floral gifts and messages and, in the end, we had to ask the nurses to redistribute some of them to one or two elderly patients whose lives might be made a little more cheery by some vases of flowers beside their beds. We just hoped nobody would mind.

When I went home that evening, this time with one of our driver-youngsters, I felt a great sense of relief, for Mrs D was where she could be cared for properly, she was looking better than she had done for about ten days, and the early medical reports gave hope for a little cautious optimism. It appeared we might have found the problem just in time.

The next morning, when I made an early call, Mrs D asked me to bring in some bras; not just any old bras but soft ones and ones that didn't have those nasty bits of wire in them. I located her drawer of underclothes and was in for a shock because I had never realised before just how many of the things Mrs Dudgeon had! There was a ... a multitudity of them, which is the only collective term I can think of for a bra mountain. They came in all sorts of shapes and colours, and I attempted to arrange them in various piles according to the qualities I imagined would make them desirable. My short-listed pile numbered about twenty-seven and, try as hard as I might, I could not decide which were the most suitable, so I bundled them all into a bag and hoped I wouldn't be arrested on the way to the hospital.

'Now, Sir, would you mind opening your bag for me... Hello, hello, hello. What 'ave we got here, then? Perhaps we should pop down to the station and have a word. Have you been in trouble before...'

The news was good that morning. A large tumour had been removed, larger than they had expected, and as a result the surgeon had taken away a good number of lymph glands as well. He remarked on the strength of Mrs D's immune system, which seemed to have had the capacity to contain the tumour within its boundaries, but we all knew we were not yet out of the woods. There were many tests still to be done, and any one of them could bring yet more sobering news. The cancer could have wandered wherever it wished.

Mrs D was lying on the bed wearing white thrombosis stockings when I arrived. They seem to be used routinely these days as a measure against the possibility of blood clots forming while patients are immobile. I was still wearing mine for the regulation period following a hip replacement, so we looked a funny pair in our white 'Teds'. They are extraordinarily difficult things to put on and to attempt to do so, in my case, would have been to have risked hip damage. In Mrs D's case, her right arm was only just movable that morning, so she certainly could not cope with hers. When the nurses came to change them, I asked if mine could also be changed and thereafter, each day, the nurses would come in saying, 'Right, Teds time now. Who's first? Duncan?' and I would pull a clean pair from my pocket and offer them to the nurse.

The fine white comfortable 'Teds' used now made me realise how things have moved on. Fifteen years ago I had a real problem with a vein in my calf, and it developed into raging phlebitis, which is rather like having a gas blowlamp played on the back of the leg, only it is slightly more unpleasant. I had been applying ice packs every few hours, but to no avail. It happened just before we were due to go away on holiday so I went to the doctor who hummed and ha'd and prescribed stockings ... what my grandmother used to call 'elastic hose': great heavy brown things that as a boy I enviously eyed up and down with thoughts of catapult elastic.

I duly trotted off to the chemist, feeling old before my time. The shop was full, and as I had already spotted one or two of my pupils within earshot, I very surreptitiously passed my prescription to the pharmacist, a hulk of a man with a deep booming voice.

'Ah right. Elastic hose! If you'd like to sit over there, MR DUDGEON, and I will be with you directly to measure you for YOUR STOCKINGS!'

Heads turned all over the chemist's shop, and two boys who were trying on sunglasses in front of a mirror, nudged one another.

'It's old Dudge. 'E's 'aving them granny stockings,' one of them whispered in a very loud voice.

'If you'd like to roll up your trouser leg, I'll measure you for the right one,' the pharmacist bawled from behind his screen. 'Looks like a 43M to me. I'll just get my tape measure. Right leg, isn't it?'

Eventually I escaped, and back at home I decided to avoid the humiliation of putting them on in front of our then young children (who were absolutely bound to ask 'Why is Daddy wearing stockings, Mummy?' at the most inconvenient moment in a crowded restaurant) and took myself into the WC. There, I rolled up the stocking and tried to stretch it over my foot. I attempted to do it while seated, then I stood and put my foot on the seat and tried again and partially succeeded, but could go no further so I sat down again, leant forwards and continued to heave. As I did so my back went 'crackkk' and a shock wave of pain went up and down my spine. I held my breath and remained motionless, then tried to relax and uncoil myself, elastic hose at half-mast around my ankle. Eventually I gave up trying to remove it and crept out, bent double, to seek Mrs

D's help. The car was packed ready to leave at that moment so I took some painkillers, Mrs Dudgeon put the stocking on, the children were bundled into the back of the motor and we set off on holiday.

Mrs Dudgeon chuckled fondly when I passed her the bag of underwear. She immediately and effortlessly selected two and gave me the remainder to take home again.

'You keep them, dearest,' I said. 'Bring them home when you come. You might need another one,' and hastily I slid the bag into a drawer, well out of sight of the local constabulary.

We had supper together several times at the hospital, which saved me the arduous task of cooking a meal when I arrived home. The truth was that I would have only eaten a sandwich because managing food preparation on two crutches is, to put it mildly, quite difficult. I always felt as though I was taking part in one of those television game shows where the participants are shown some impossible feat and are then expected to complete the task without help. It looked easy but wasn't, and I had already broken a number of pieces of china, dropped a pan of bacon (much to the dog's delight), not to mention having shut my head in the fridge door which swung swiftly closed while I was reaching into the lower shelves.

Mrs D had often eaten with me at the other hospital and it was a delightfully sociable thing to do, but somehow we couldn't quite persuade ourselves that it was a holiday and that we were in a hotel; it may have had something to do with the nurses who kept 'popping' in to take Mrs D's temperature and blood pressure, usually in between the main course and dessert. We've been to some interesting hotels where the service is annoyingly attentive, but none that run to those extremes.

27

The next morning, as I arrived, the physiotherapist was just finishing her spell with Mrs D.

'Yeah well, it's all in the pamphlet, love. Just do the exercises it says and you'll be all right, yeah? Get your arm moving again, that's the thing, luvvie. Any problems and give me a shout, yeah? I'll pop in and see you tomorrow, okay?'

We had been thoroughly spoiled by Megan, which meant that Trixie, for that was her name, was on a hiding to nothing before she even opened her mouth (and there was plenty of it). I had spotted her several days previously when we had been to see the Professor, and came to the conclusion that she was ... what our children would call 'rough'. She was about fifty going on twenty-two with masses of bleached blonde hair, and she looked as though a sizeable proportion of every day was spent on the sunbed. She was nut-brown and wizened; sort of overcooked like a crunchy rasher of bacon that one would fling out of the back door for the dog to eat in the garden. Being so desperately tanned seemed an odd statement to make in an oncology ward where skin cancers were being treated on a daily basis, but live and let live; I suppose it's up to her if she wishes to frazzle herself. What Mrs D found less than helpful was that Trixie had not attempted to work through the exercises with her.

Knowing from my own experience how important that foundation session is, I sat on the bed with Mrs D and we practised the exercises together; lifting the operated arm with the good arm, 'brushing the hair', 'scratching the back' and rolling the shoulders forward and then backwards. I did my best Megan impression:

'Just do it a little to begin with. Each time you do it, your arm will move a little more. Don't go beyond the point where it hurts, only up to it. Well done. How does that feel? Sore? Poor love. Rest now, and relax. It's important to know how to relax. Do it again in an hour. Little and often to begin with' and so on ... perhaps I should have been a physiotherapist.

We knew that some of the pathology tests on the tumour would take several weeks to come through, but when the quietly spoken Professor came in he was still optimistic and patted Mrs D's hand. When she made some comment about her wound, he looked up as though surprised.

'Do you mean you've looked at it already?'

'Why of course,' said my wife, equally surprised. 'The nurses changed my dressing, so naturally, I looked. We both did. We looked together.'

'Goodness,' he chuckled, 'most women can't bear to look for days. Brave girl, brave girl,' he said in genuine admiration.

'The nurses all think it's a wonderful incision; you're very clever.'

'Well,' he said thoughtfully, 'I promise you I'm not often told that. I really am the enemy for wives and husbands, and they don't thank me for what I have to do. The men are the worst, Mrs Dudgeon. You're very fortunate.' He nodded in my direction.

Mrs D asked him what he meant, given that all patients must want to be rid of their cancers, and he explained how men in particular can make life difficult and have been known to tear up the Consent Form in a proprietorial attempt to prevent a full mastectomy occurring. We were shocked, but it was later repeated to us in different ways by nurses and breast counsellors. It explained why I often sensed that until they had got to know us, particularly me, there was always an air of mistrust, of wariness, as though they would have liked to have asked quietly of Mrs D, '... and how has HE been about it?'

Before long, we were counting the days until Mrs D came out of hospital. She was making good progress, sometimes sad and weepy, but usually on top of the world and looking remarkably well. Without doubt, she remembers the drains as being the worst bit. Not drain drains, you understand, not the hospital's drains but hers, that is in-the-wound-type-drains which, of course, have to come out when they have done their job, a somewhat mucky, uncomfortable procedure as I had discovered a few weeks before. It's just ... a nasty feeling, but it is always over very quickly. What actually happened had us in fits of laughter afterwards but at the time, it was not at all funny and it provided the nudge towards a really good howl, which I am sure is inevitable and probably very beneficial for every woman in this unenviable position.

Now, if you are squeamish or just about to eat supper, I suggest you might prefer to skip this next bit, which will, of course, make it compulsive reading for everyone; just don't send me any cleaning bills, please.

The nurses came with a tray of swabs and other accoutrements of drain removal, and Mrs D tried to sit back and relax as the fine tube was slowly drawn out from under her arm. It hurt like billy-ho in a tummy-churning sort of way, but she was all right until after it was all over, when she heard the nurse say agitatedly to the other nurse, 'Oh no! Quick! There's serious fluid running out of here,' which prompted the other nurse to move quickly to Mrs D's side and, not surprisingly, she had visions of her very life-sap running away and was understandably frightened.

After a while, they dressed the wound, cleared up and left her, not realising she was so disturbed by the experience and as soon as the door was shut, the poor love began to sob; a little to begin with and then more and more, whereupon one of the nurses happened to return and found her in a state.

'Oh darling, whatever is the matter? What has upset you?' the nurse asked, sitting on the bed to comfort her, for it was the first time she had seen Mrs D have a really good cry all week.

'I don't want to lose serious fluid. How serious was it? It frightened me. What's wrong with it? Tell me, please. I don't mind how bad it was. Tell me the truth.'

Unable to keep a straight face, the nurse broke into a smile.

'You silly old thing,' she said, squeezing her hand, 'it's not serious fluid, it's serous fluid, you know, like serum; tissue fluids.'

Mrs D looked at her. 'You mean it's not serious after all?'

'Not at all,' the nurse replied, laughing.

'Why did you look at Chris in such a worried way, then?'

'Worried way? No, I wasn't worried. It was about to run down your nightie, that's all. It's such a pretty nightie, I didn't want to spoil it.'

28

One evening, I arrived at the hospital to see Mrs D and decided to visit the Gents on the way to the ward. I admit that I was tired because the routine of the previous few days had been quite gruelling; journeys to see Mrs Dudgeon a couple of times each day, trips to my hospital for physiotherapy and generally keeping everything going at home had been a fair strain.

I balanced on my crutches and pushed the heavy, spring-loaded loo door open only to be confronted by another, equally heavy one, a privacy door, and a short dark lobby in between. I had developed the knack of opening doors, which basically is to brace oneself, give the door a good shove, wedge the crutch rubber at the base of the open door and then swing through as quickly as possible. I managed to get into the inner sanctum, answered the call of nature and turned to go out. I pulled the door open, wedged it and went through, then I pulled the next one and, as I moved to wedge that, the first whacked into my back, knocking me forwards into the half-open second door. I stood in the dark vestibule recoiling from the battering, then took half a pace forwards to grasp the handle just as another gent pushed it open from the other side with a gusto which sent me flying backwards again into the inner door. He was enormously apologetic, helped me to stand up again, lent me a handkerchief to dab my nose and applied an impressive degree of force to my bent crutch in order to render it usable once more.

When I walked into Mrs D's room a few minutes later, she looked up from her chair and said 'Hello dear, you look weary,' but I didn't have the heart to tell her I'd simply been trying to go to the loo. It brought home to me once again how difficult life must be for those who do not have full mobility, and fire doors, the heavy brutes with automatic closing devices, are one of the worst culprits.

I think that was the night when my back ached so much that I stretched out flat on Mrs Dudgeon's hospital bed, and it was so wonderful to be horizontal that I promptly fell asleep. Apparently the nurses came and went and I slumbered and snored until it was getting quite late and my lift arrived. I'm afraid I wasn't much of a visitor for Mrs D that night, and as I left, the nurses all made great play of my snoozing.

'We'll get a double bed in tomorrow,' one said, and another made a quip about men having no stamina for coping at home while their wives were in hospital. My reply was, I am afraid, quite unrepeatable in these pages.

The next day we hoped that Mrs D would be allowed to come home, although there was some question about whether her red blood cell count was adequate for her to be released. Fortunately, they decided she could manage as she was, without a transfusion, on the strict condition that she drank plenty of red wine to help her blood to restore itself. She looked at me with glee as I listened to her relate all the Professor had said during his rounds, and she suggested that we might be able to get a wine box on prescription.

'I doubt it very much. If you could, I think there would be a sudden and remarkable increase in the number of anaemic patients queueing at the doctor's surgery,' I said, not wishing to dampen her optimism.

I have to say that Mrs D was very conscientious about all the advice she was given in hospital, but none more so than that particular piece. I offered to buy red grape juice, but she was adamant. 'Red wine was what they said, and red wine it will be,' she chided me with a chuckle. I must say, it was extraordinary how rapidly her haemaglobin count reverted to somewhere near normal in a matter of a few weeks.

As often happens, and it is a good reason always to try to have someone with you during crucial medical appointments, the Professor had said something, almost in passing, which Mrs D had not really taken on board until she dwelt on his words later.

'Well done,' he said, 'you've got through this first stage very well.' Then he mentioned again how strong Mrs Dudgeon's immune system had been to cope with the tumour and she related how, being on leave to look after me, she had had a little more time than usual to dress, and that was how she had first noticed the blemish in the mirror as the sunlight shone across her bosom. In the normal busy-ness of a working week, she is convinced to this day that it would have remained unnoticed. He told her how fortunate she was and how wise she had been not to lose a moment before seeking help.

The breast counsellor visited to advise on how Mrs D should look after herself and also to provide her with a simple prosthesis which would, at least temporarily, give her the confidence of a reasonably normal shape.

'What size are you, love?' she asked.

'A 36B,' said Mrs D and the nurse disappeared for a few minutes and returned with two small polythene bags.

'There you are. One for a spare. Let's try it.'

Mrs D fed the soft white bundle into her bra.

'Hmm,' said the nurse, examining the resulting profile. 'Been exaggerating a little, have we my dear? I might be wrong, but I think you are an A cup. Sorry to disillusion you,' and with that she went off with a smile to seek a slightly smaller version.

It was a good job that the friend who brought us back from the hospital had a large car, because the 'florist's shop' seemed to consume a huge amount of space. We found a jolly porter who didn't seem to mind lugging the equivalent of a Chelsea Flower Show stand out to the car, and we finally packed it all in. Then it was time to make our goodbyes and to thank all the nursing staff who had been so incredibly kind to Mrs D. To witness those farewells was to understand the extent to which their lives are dedicated to their work. It was profoundly moving, and I believe a mark of the very special empathy which grows between women in a crisis situation which, frankly, only women can completely comprehend.

Not for the first time in the previous six months we had a hospital homecoming and, just as I had found, the effort of achieving it was almost too much for Mrs D, so we packed her off to bed where the children all went to see her until her eyelids drooped and she slept. It was wonderful to feel she was back with us again, and, perhaps rather selfishly, I was also relieved not to be making any more journeys to the hospital. The constant movement and lack of rest had been hugely demanding, and my overworked muscles cried out for a little more time in the horizontal than I had allowed them. By comparison, it was light relief to look after Mrs D in the bedroom or in the living room, and when we needed to collapse, we could do so together in the sunny, afternoon privacy of our own home.

Several times, we remarked on how fortunate we were that our children were all in their teens or twenties. We tried to imagine how we would be coping if they were all much younger and needing our constant attention. It was not a happy thought. What actually happened was that one of the college-age daughters swung into action without being prompted and not only shopped for the family but also cooked for us all, and very competent she was too. She took pleasure in preparing the most excellent, appetising meals and generally doing anything she could to help. More than once I reflected that the wheel had turned full circle for all of them, and that the gentle pressure to shrug off the fecklessness of teenage years had ushered them into adulthood in a way that I might previously have doubted was possible. It was a heartwarming time which brought strength to the two of us when we might otherwise have just eaten cheese sandwiches, drunk lots of red wine and felt too exhausted to move. It was also a far-cry from the days when Mrs D and I would receive a phone call from one of the children while we were travelling somewhere.

'Hi Mum,' one would say, out of the blue, 'how do you

turn the grill on?' or, 'You know this pizza, do you take all the plastic stuff off before it goes in the oven?' or, the one we will remember for all time … 'Mum, where's the washing machine?'

29

It never ceases to amaze me how, when people have a favourite hobby-horse, they will, generally with the sensitivity of a rhinoceros, thrust their own pet beliefs upon you. With the best intentions in the world, acquaintances who barely knew us would write, phone, or worse still, stop us in the middle of the High Street just at the moment we had, very visibly, reached our exhaustion point and were desperate to get back to the car.

'Oh Duncan. How are you? You ought to throw away those crutches, you know. I met someone who is the most amazing healer. He'd have you up and walking around in no time. You don't even have to visit him because he does this incredible thing where you phone him and then massage your leg with the phone while he directs these fantastic beams down into you...'

As our eloquent children would say, 'Yeah, right...'

Shortly after Mrs D returned home from hospital, an acquaintance called. I answered the phone and passed it to her with a silently-mouthed indication of who was calling. I should have said Mrs D was asleep but I didn't, and afterwards I could have kicked myself.

'It's Petunia...' I whispered and I passed the phone to my wife. Mrs D explained that she was home again and that, yes, she had had a mastectomy. Yes, the rumours were true. I heard her say 'Yes, all of it,' and then later, in a slightly puzzled tone, 'No they didn't,' and later still, 'They don't actually do that,' and her manner became just a little chilly. After far too long, the phone call ended with Mrs D saying,

156

'Well, that's very kind of you, Petunia. I may do that. Thank you. Goodbye.'

'Not if I see you coming first, I won't,' she said with uncharacteristic annoyance in her voice, as she put the receiver noisily back on its rest.

Petunia had once been a nurse before she branched out into whacky therapies which, in my books, makes her twice as dangerous as those who are just plain whacky and have no knowledge. She had asked Mrs D whether they had removed all of her breast and she had replied truthfully, in the affirmative.

'What, all of it?' Petunia had asked. 'Do you really mean all of it?' and when Mrs D had replied that they had, she said, 'What, do you mean they didn't even leave you with a nipple?'

'How the hell does she suppose I'm going to keep a nipple on my chest if they've taken my breast away?' Mrs D said angrily. 'Some people are unbelievable. How did she think that phone call could possibly help me in my present situation?' and she burst into tears. For a few moments, I felt as though all the encouragement, and all the confidence-inspiring talks we had shared, had been dashed to nothing by a thoughtless, five-minute phone call. It wasn't so of course, but it was an unnecessary low point and, I have to say, one which might have brought about Petunia's very sticky end.

Later in the call Petunia had then offered Mrs Dudgeon a free session of her crystal-centring therapy with a promise of leaflets about it to follow in the post.

'It's amazing!' (It always is) 'There are only three practitioners in the whole world and I am one of them.' (Uh oh) 'Any time you want I could start you off on a course. It will cleanse your system of all the negative vibrations that cancer cells release. You'll begin to feel better straight away. I've treated twenty-three million people already, and every one of them now has a clean bill of health...'

I wouldn't let Petunia near my dog, let alone my family. She really should carry a very serious health warning, along the lines of, 'Keep away from me ... I'm not only dangerous, I'm totally bonkers!'

* * *

We continued to receive hosts of letters, cards and gifts, all wishing Mrs Dudgeon well. Some were less than tactful. In fact, let's be honest, some of them, if they hadn't been so funny, would have been down-right insulting.

One day a package arrived from someone we hadn't seen for years. She had heard Mrs D had not been well so she sent ... a jar of herbal tea. Actually, it didn't look like tea, it looked like the prunings from my hawthorn hedge. I think it probably was. There was a leaflet with the 'tea' explaining that there were three varieties in the series to suit the three main human characteristics, because you see ... there are only three. You may have thought there were more, (so did I actually), but no, there are three 'dochas' according to ancient Indian custom.

Our benefactor was faced with an interesting dilemma: which one to send? Here is an extract from the 'docha' description she selected for Mrs D. Presumably this portrays Mrs Dudgeon and her personality:

'Your laidback attitude can sometimes go too far, leading to a sluggish mind and body.'

Oh well, that's really kind of you. Thank you so much. How about this:

'You need get up and go, try to boost your energy and get out of the rut.'

Now which rut would that be?

'Good points (Ah!): Solid and dependable, you're a loving partner and the perfect person to have around in a crisis.'

That's a bit better. I have to agree that in the last few crises I have been in, I have tended to look for that perfect chum with the sluggish, laidback mind and body. It fills you with such extraordinary confidence at a time of desperate need.

158

Mrs D and I discussed it and tried to imagine sending someone a gift like that, and we decided that ... we probably wouldn't.

Just after my back operation, I received a letter from an acquaintance, and it's worth noting here that these people are never what you would really call 'friends', they are just ... people you happen to know; the word leeches comes to mind, but it is too cruel to apply it (to most of them).

'Dear Duncan,' the note read, 'I was so sorry to learn that you have been in hospital again for your back. How annoying for you. I must say that in my experience, surgery rarely does much good, indeed it may do a great deal of harm. It interrupts the flow of energy through the body and only certain sorts of therapy can then release the tensions which will bind you for ever if you are not vigilant. (Oh my goodness! But wait for it...) I happen to have come across an amazing (!) new therapy; you may be surprised to learn that it involves wearing magnetic Wellington boots for an hour a day. The energy which is blocking the channels of your...'

I wouldn't like you to think me an ungrateful person, for I am not, but I do resent these appalling intrusions. However, I am a big softy at heart and as a result, at nine p.m. tonight and every night, I know that there is a whole network of healers who will be zooming in on my vertebrae because I didn't have the courage to say 'No' for fear of offending someone. In my shed, I have a beautifully constructed, six-foot-high wooden pyramid covered in aluminium baking foil in which I am supposed to curl tightly into a ball and sleep every night (clearly, they do not understand my problem). I also have a pair of shiny silver rubber boots which are now well-chewed as the dog loves to chase around the garden with them in his mouth.

In the larder we have packets of Betalife 'revitalising therapy', based, of course, on extracts of a very rare desert cactus, *Ivanidea itscrapitus*, which only grows in Morocco; a bottle of wine made from over-ripe, pressed Brussels sprouts, and a packet of dried substance which I am sure the local constabulary might be very interested to see. People have been so thoughtful.

Such consideration knows no bounds. After a long period of horizontal following a damaged disc years ago, a 'friend', who had aspirations of being a counsellor, came to visit, and she actually had the audacity to ask, with very little preamble, whether I was able to manage a satisfactory sex-life.

After I had wiped up my cup of coffee, having coughed and spluttered it all over the bedspread, I must have replied, but I cannot for the life of me remember how. It transpired that the lady concerned had once helped handicapped partners to achieve ... satisfactory sex-lives and, for some bizarre reason, she thought that Mrs D and I could do with a helping hand. The mind boggles. I've often wondered what would have happened if I had said, 'Oh my goodness, yes ... just exactly what we need. When are you free to come?' (so to speak).

Now I must redress the balance. Our friends, and I use the term advisedly in this instance, knowing what I was up against kitchen-wise, began to visit daily and brought delicious offerings. One came bearing several shepherd's pies for the freezer, another with chicken pies and yet another with cakes. The word had also got around that red wine was the order of the day, and a steady trickle of Mrs D's fortifying tonic arrived. Friends even came to collect the dog en route to the countryside for a Sunday walk. Everyone who knew us well was wonderful and did everything they could to support us. None of them tried to sell us their batty theories, present anything whacky or even massage our feet, it was just ... good old-fashioned, unconditional friendship at its very best. I am sure I don't need to tell you that there's nothing quite like it for lifting the spirits.

Meanwhile, I must just go and get my hood, a head-enveloping bag with eyeholes which must be worn daily at strict times, prescribed by a set of tables which describe the sun's zenith. I then have to face due south, sit upright in my chair and play a tape of the sea splashing on the beach. We keep the hood in the out-house now for, believe it or not, this malodorous linen bag is full of rotting seaweed. It smells so

160

awful that when I put it on even the dog runs away from it with his tail firmly between his legs.

I really must develop a polite, firm technique for saying 'No' to people.

30

The bill for my hip prosthesis came through a few days after Mrs D had come home from hospital. I picked up the mail from the mat and carried it through to where we were sitting enjoying breakfast. Surprised, I remarked upon its cost just before the children came in and began their guessing game.

'Good gracious!' I said, 'do you know the prosthesis cost two thousand two hundred and seventy-four pounds.'

'Heavens,' said Mrs D, 'it's just as well I didn't have the B cup, isn't it? What on earth would they have charged me for that?'

A little later that day I went to the office for half an hour to sign some papers and to check that they were still missing me. I had only been there a few minutes when Mrs Dudgeon phoned through to say she had had a call from the Professor. Sod's law dictates that that sort of thing happens. It was the first time I had left her side for about a week. I hurried home to find Mrs D visibly shaken.

'It's good news and bad,' she said. 'They have some of the results through now. It has spread, but only a little. It was found in the lymph glands, but only just. It was caught early, but it means that I have to have chemotherapy and possibly radiotherapy as well.'

We sank down into chairs to absorb the news. We hadn't had any way of judging what might follow the surgery, and even at that point, the test results were incomplete. The news was all made worse by Mrs D's memories of her older sister dying of cancer and having a very traumatic time with chemotherapy. It isn't easy to come to terms with memories such as those, although we both knew that the advances in such treatments had moved on in great strides since the days she remembered.

Almost as an antidote to the news, we planned a couple of days away to visit parents and relax. It had been a long haul since we had been to Wales, and it now appeared that we were about to embark on another one. The Professor had indicated that, although a cancer specialist would decide her precise treatment, it was likely to last for six months.

One of the positive responses we were able to make was to begin to read more about breast cancer. We found a wealth of material available: books on diets, therapies and on generally managing one's well-being to enable the body to have the best chance of fighting the invasive cell growths. It was empowering, if only because at last there seemed to be something we could do. There was no need to stand still and wait for all the treatment to happen; it was possible to, at least partially, own the problem which hitherto seemed to have been driven by medics and the urgency of the situation.

Our children were amused by the subtle changes in Mrs D's diet although, as a family with two vegetarian girls, we had always eaten wisely, tending towards fish, legumes, vegetables and the super-cancer-fighter, broccoli. Quantities of broccoli in the supermarket trolley doubled overnight, intake of fruit was trebled, tomatoes appeared everywhere, coffee was relegated to the past and we could well have engaged a trawler of our own to bring home the fish we needed to meet the family's needs. It was very satisfying, except that none of us had quite expected the extent of the problem which afflicts all vegetarians ... wind.

Anyone who has ever worked with horses or cattle knows instinctively what happens when considerable quantities of plants are eaten; indeed I recall riding in a pony and trap and realising for the first time that it was not such a romantic experience as it might at first appear. Every two minutes, the horse would blow off a stream of excruciating, toxic fumes, making the driver and myself draw our scarves around our faces. What you might, I suppose, call a horse and fart.

For years I had been teaching the wisdom of the Western world turning towards a more vegetarian diet, based purely upon the relative agricultural efficiencies of producing plant protein and animal protein. I now wish to take back all I ever said in the classroom. It is patently nonsense. If we all make serious efforts to become vegetarians, it is clear that the old London 'pea-soupers' will be but a wispy mist compared to that which will choke our cities and towns as we all become serious about our intake of broccoli, sprouts, lentils and other sources of plant protein. The end of mankind as we know it will be just around the corner. Night after night the Dudgeon household flung open windows, took strolls around the garden and pleaded with the dog to come into the house again. For years, we had all dived towards the door to escape his noxious emissions, and now the tables were turned.

One of the other delicate little matters we had to cope with was the problem of consuming codeine as an analgesic. For a few weeks we were both taking it and it does, to put it mildly, 'bind one', as my grandmother would have said. The effects are remarkable and, being a lateral thinker, I was doing my best to think of alternative uses for the substance. Land reclamation of marshlands came readily to mind; I am convinced it has a future way beyond that of acting as a painkiller.

We both took a gentle laxative before breakfast each morning, because to fail to manage the situation well was to suffer greatly by the evening. Without wishing to be in any way distasteful about these matters, it is actually one of the more surprising side effects of a hip operation that it is very difficult to sit on the throne. Raised toilet seats are provided so that the new joint is not bent upwards to an extreme degree, but the seat cannot help with the fundamental problem, that surgery in that area, as all mothers will know from post-natal days, can make life very uncomfortable. On many occasions in the past, whilst on morphine, which has a similar effect, I staggered bowlegged from the WC with eyes smarting, and lurched towards the little brown bottle of syrupy liquid which I had omitted to take on the previous day.

Mrs D was much more organised and poured out the 'Rocketlax' as she boiled the kettle for breakfast tea.

'Duncan,' she would say, 'your plumbing-kit is here,' and we would both simultaneously swig down the thick goo. If we had been a little more organised, we might have staggered our intake to avoid what became a common occurrence when we would both, a few hours later, need the appropriate facilities at the same time. I would lurch through the hall with a puckered little expression on my face and meet Mrs D with the same sort of countenance, whereupon we would have a very short diplomatic discussion about whose needs were most urgent and the loser would about turn and race off to find alternative accommodation. It always happened at the same time which, given the inevitable variations in the working of the human bowel, was quite remarkable. Enough said.

The day came when we had to attend Mrs D's follow-up appointment to have a very considerable number of clips removed from her wound and to meet the oncologist for the first time. The Professor was delighted with the physical success of the operation and rightly so; each of the professionals who had seen her incision remarked that it was one of the finest they had ever seen. We still look at it together and remark upon its smoothness. To those who may have recently faced this ordeal, or perhaps are crazy enough to read this book pre-operatively, I would say one thing: 'Be patient with your wound.' Whatever it looks like to begin with, however alarmed you may feel about it, it will settle down; but it takes time. We enacted a touching little ritual each night before bed whereby, very gently, I would apply a fine cream to Mrs D's wound. It was not only good for the physical processes but the psychological ones as well. As Mrs D said, not only did it speak to her of my care for her but also of acceptance. I hope you will not mind me sharing that little piece of advice from the privacy of our bedroom. I promise it will be the first and the last.

31

We have often remarked that it was extraordinarily fortunate that our times in hospital did not coincide. In an ideal world, of course, neither of us would have had anything wrong and Mrs D would certainly not have had cancer. But her discovery, made as it was just as I emerged from hospital, meant that we missed the worst possible scenario which was both to be in hospital, different ones, at the same time. We also said that it was damned efficient to concentrate our times of great need into one period. Although partly a tongue-in-cheek comment, it was true. If I had made a recovery and then Mrs D had been ill, our consecutive times of hospitalisation, treatment and convalescence might have lasted for two years!

By the time Mrs D's treatment began, I was driving again. After five months of being unable to take the car out, it was exhilarating to be behind the wheel once more. Mrs Dudgeon was still too sore from her surgery to risk driving, so even this detail of the meshing of our inabilities was extremely fortunate. We felt like Jack Sprat and his wife.

The first day of Mrs D's treatment was, to put it mildly, rather hectic. It had been decided that, for very good reasons, the two components, radiotherapy and chemotherapy, should occur at two different hospitals. Fortunately, one of them was also the hospital I attended for physiotherapy; had it not been, I suspect life would have become quite unmanageable. As it was, we dashed from one, where the radiotherapy measurements, calculations and the programming 'dummy-run' were organised, grabbed lunch and hared off in the opposite direction to the second. There, Mrs D had scans, X-rays and other checks before we were taken to the rooms where the chemotherapy was administered.

Throughout our treatments, we have been extraordinarily fortunate in having the most wonderful staff to care for us. When we returned to the ward where Mrs D had had her surgery, it was as though we were returning to the bosom of the family. During the previous week, I had, quite by chance, been to the same ward with one of our teenagers, who had had day surgery for impacted wisdom teeth, so I had a good idea of what Mrs D might expect when she returned.

On that occasion, from the moment I walked in with my son, everyone wished to know how Mrs D was.

'I've never seen so many flowers delivered for anyone,' the receptionist said. 'How is your wife? Give her my best wishes.'

And on the ward, the same pattern was repeated.

'How is she? Give her our love. We'll be seeing you next week for the chemo, won't we?'

It was also touching that they were concerned for my progress and how we had coped. What a pair we must have seemed. Truth to tell, we must have been a source of concern to them.

The oncologist, who from that moment onwards became a major figure in our lives, was a delightful man. He was a quietly spoken man with a face which was usually wreathed in welcoming smiles. He was of Middle-Eastern origin, and spoke with a measured, gentle voice which seemed to breathe assurance as he discussed the treatment, its possible side-effects and answered our many questions.

The actual administration of the chemotherapy was a hurdle which Mrs D crossed with little discomfort. No one likes having blood tests, or needles taped to veins in the back of the hand, but it is all routine hospital work. There is a good deal of waiting to be endured, as the chemo can only proceed following a satisfactory blood test. It turned out that the red wine and good food had restored Mrs D's cell count, and within a few hours we were ready to leave with different tablets to be taken at various intervals during the week.

'Oh,' said the Jordanian doctor as we were about to leave. 'The frilly knickers.'

I stopped in my tracks.

'I beg your pardon?' I asked incredulously, not believing what I had heard.

'The f-o-l-i-n-e-e-c k-a-c-i-d,' he repeated deliberately in his accent, which had somehow blurred the words. When I explained that I thought he had said 'frilly knickers', he roared with laughter and said,

'No, no; I said, "foleenikcacid" not "forillynickers", and managed to repeat it again so that it sounded just as it had the first time so that we all heard it and laughed. Dear man. We loved him, and his self-deprecating tales of his lively young family.

One hears many different stories of chemotherapy. It is such a big word: emotive, dark, brooding and threatening, but it needn't always be so. True, the chemicals are poisonous and designed to kill unwanted cells; true, there are often undesirable side-effects such as nausea and hair loss, but it is also true that the highly refined drugs administered today are very different from the early haphazard chemotherapy agents, and they do not always produce all the side-effects. If, for example, one feels nauseous and unwell, it is possible to control it and if one loses one's hair, society's trends for zero hair styles mean that it is not the scourge it once was. Be honest, if you walk through the High Street today, how many people do you see now with shaved heads? How many of them are on chemotherapy? Possibly some, but not many. It is all much easier than it was.

We were told a story by an oncologist which concerned a clinic he had once been responsible for, as it happened, for men. He used to watch from his room as his patients would arrive, park their cars and in some cases be sick in the car park long before they reached the treatment room. The point of his story is that one can allow one's fears to grow to the point where the anxieties will actually shape one's physical responses.

It doesn't have to be so. Chemotherapy actually brings life and Mrs D used to remember that positive thought and focus on it as the drugs were being given to her and in the weeks afterwards when, at times, she felt physically knocked sideways by it. The power of the mind is a great and mysterious healer and we were both determined not to become *victims* of our circumstances.

The process by which one acclimatises to serious illness and its treatment is, as I have remarked before, an extraordinary one. Not only the patient comes to terms with all it entails, but whole families do also. Expressions such as 'Mum's chemo' and 'Mum's cancer' become commonplace in a manner one could never have envisaged weeks or months before. It can't always be easy to remain positive about such things; we met many people in our travels who were in a far worse state than Mrs D, and we regularly gave thanks for the relatively straightforward nature of her disease. That may sound odd, not least because breast cancer is a highly emotive subject and guaranteed to frighten. But our thoughts on the matter now, with hindsight, are that it could have been far worse, and that any women with doubts about their well-being should straightaway seek help, for so often it is the delaying which brings about the complex and sometimes insoluble problems.

If you have doubts, just go. Go to the doctor; badger for mammograms; seek help; get second opinions, but don't rest if you feel something is not as it should be. It is your life, and to be straightforward about it, you have approximately one of them (as far as we know that is).

Mrs D certainly didn't feel on top of the world during her chemo and radiotherapy for, without doubt, it is debilitating. It produced peculiar feelings, apart from periods of gross tiredness. Odd tastes in the mouth; the sort of malaise one might feel after a bad bout of flu; nausea which never quite gets going but affects what you feel like eating, much as many women suffer in pregnancy; and some soreness at the site of the radiotherapy bombardment ... but all were manageable symptoms. Maybe we had been well prepared for feeling grotty. My own experiences with drugs had doubtless paved the way for

169

accepting that, however unpleasant while they last, these things do eventually pass.

We were both struck by the sheer numbers of people who at any one time are receiving treatment for cancer. Bearing in mind that we only visited a couple of hospital departments during Mrs D's treatment and that presumably the same can be found in any town or city, one glimpsed the enormity of the problem. This was particularly noticeable in the radiotherapy unit, where patients were all attending on a daily basis for five or six weeks but each treatment lasted only a few minutes. The staff, forever cheerful and positive, spent every moment of their working day doing nothing but zapping tumours or, as in Mrs D's case, irradiating surgical sites where tumours had been removed. In the waiting rooms one would find one's mind wondering: 'What is he here for?' 'What story could she tell?', and of course sometimes patients talked and stories did unfold.

I must confess to having something of a weakness for people-watching. It affects me mostly on trains, in waiting rooms and in supermarkets. I cannot help it; it is almost addictive. Often, Mrs D will tell me to bring something to read, knowing we may have to endure a long wait, but I rarely do. Instead, I sit and watch people. Even when nothing remarkable occurs, I am fascinated by how people dress, their mannerisms and their behaviour. The disadvantage of being so thoroughly observant is that sometimes one can be irritated by the most insignificant fact.

'Do you know,' I might say to Mrs D, 'that woman at the check-out didn't look at us once. She just waved all the groceries across the scanner and shoved them down the conveyor ... and did you notice she was wearing the same necklace we gave to...'

Mrs D will sensibly and honestly reply that she barely noticed it was a woman, let alone noticed where she was looking; and that it could, in fact, have been anybody sitting there. But then, you see, Mrs D is not afflicted with this compulsion.

On one particular morning a weary-looking, elderly man sat opposite us. He made himself comfortable and read his paper, a tabloid. He studied page three for a while, and shortly afterwards he was joined by a late-middle-aged man and a younger person who was very clearly a son. After a few minutes the two older men turned and recognised one another.

'Hello, Dick,' said the father, rather too loudly so that the whole waiting room could hear, 'I haven't seen you for ages. What are you in here for, then?'

The older man mumbled, looking somewhat embarrassed, but his tactless friend continued.

'Eh?'

'Prostrate,' he replied a little louder.

'Mmm, well, well,' said the other, 'fancy that. Have you met my boy?' he asked, indicating the large forty-year-old sitting beside him, who was looking as though he could have quite cheerfully smothered his father. The two nodded.

'Dad, I'm not your boy any more,' said the son quietly to the father. 'I'm forty-one next year.'

'Nah. You'll always be my boy. Don't you like me saying that? Do I embarrass you? You're too soft, that's your trouble,' all at the top of his voice.

Fortunately, he was called for his appointment and the two rose to go before there was a serious outbreak of patricide. The older man visibly relaxed and looked at us with a tiny wince of apology.

The chair next to him was then taken by a bespectacled man who sat down, took out his book, wedged his glasses on the top of his head and proceeded to read with his nose no more than two inches from the pages. I have never seen anyone do that before and, I must confess, I was fascinated. Surely, I thought, it would have been more comfortable to have alleviated his extreme short-sightedness by wearing an alternative pair of specs. Mrs D had also noticed. She leaned towards me and whispered in my ear,

'I think that is what you might call having your nose stuck in a book.'

I am glad that soon after we were called for Mrs D's appointment, because every time I looked up, try as hard as I might, I began to break into the first sniggers of uncontrollable laughter. It may have been a release of tension, but had I stayed, I am sure I would have caused great offence.

Part of the setting-up process for the radiotherapy involves making very precise measurements and then marking the body so that each time the patient returns, it is a straightforward matter to achieve the correct alignment. The datum points are actually made with two very tiny, very permanent tattoos. No ordinary pen mark could survive five weeks of wear and tear, so I can understand why it is done, although having said that I am still trying to scrub Mr T's graffiti from my own leg.

Thinking the children would be impressed by their mother having a couple of tattoos, she told them about the marks when we arrived home. One needs to bear in mind that our children have between them thirteen ear-piercings, one pierced nose, one pierced navel and several other things they have probably omitted to tell us about. Their reaction to the tattoos was very revealing.

'Are you serious?' they asked, clearly appalled at the thought. 'Tattoos? You mean, like, forever-tattoos?'

Mrs D nodded, realising that far from being proud of their Mum's newly established trendy development, they were horrified.

'Mum, how can you be so chilled about it? It will be there for ever, you know, like ... always. How could you let them do that to you?'

It didn't seem to occur to them that what lay between those two tiny marks was far, far worse than anything a tattooist could ever inflict; somehow the paradox never struck them. Mrs D and I talked about it and realised that one of the great things about being young is that when life becomes too difficult, you just blank it out. How wonderful! All I can do is to wish them many years of blissful ignorance ... before they wake to some of the harsher realities of life.

172

32

'Try to swing your pelvis as you bring your leg forward. That's it. Keep your head up. Look in the mirror. Now keep the weight on the new hip. Keep walking. Turn now and come back towards me. Good, good. Well done. Much, much better. Can you feel the difference?'

I could. It hurt like mad. Megan was 'teaching me how to walk again'. After months of trying to shift weight onto the side which didn't hurt, I was now suffering a considerable amount of pain, sometimes at nights, but always while I walked without crutches or sticks. Megan's diagnosis was that I had moved my 'centre' so far to the right that everything felt strained. When she stood me up straight, it felt far from straight; it felt uncomfortably unnatural.

'That's what you've got to achieve,' she said. 'You have to re-train all those muscles and ligaments.'

What was most alarming was that when I stood still, my new leg seemed to be about an inch longer than the other one. I could slip a paperback beneath the unaffected foot, and then I felt normal again. It wasn't actually so because the measurements said otherwise, apart from which, I had been told that the surgeons all vie with one another for the most perfectly matched leg lengths. I was sure Mr T's tape measure hadn't slipped to that extent.

I had often imagined the process which must happen on the operating table. Having been a bit of a DIY enthusiast in my time, I could visualise him, mallet in one hand, tape measure held in the other. Rather like knocking a window frame into an opening in a wall, it is crucial to make sure that the frame is set in line with the brickwork.

Tap, Tap. Two centimetres to go. Tap, tap, tap.

'Damn! Too far.'

Swing outside and knock it back again. Start again. Now ... concentrate.

Megan assured me that when the settling down had finished, all would be well.

One has to do an immense amount of trusting during any treatment, for the reality is we have no way of knowing the outcome and no way of evaluating what is being offered. Even after treatment is successful, one still cannot know for certain what would have happened if ... but during the process, when there is often a startling lack of evidence concerning its efficacy, one just trusts.

On the days when Mrs D was halfway through her treatment and feeling less than perky, we thought about how ironic it was that she had never actually been unwell, as such, with her cancer. The only things which had made her feel unwell were clearly the surgery, and later the chemotherapy and the radiotherapy. She had joined the wagon feeling perfectly fit and well, and then steadily declined thereafter. It was an odd concept, and all one could do was trust that the short-term consequences of the treatment were going to produce dividends in the long term.

The nature of chemotherapy, which is usually a cyclical affair based on, for example, two weeks of treatment and two weeks of recovery, followed by two weeks of treatment and so on, means that one has to accept that, just as the effects wear off and one has a 'good week', it will be necessary to return to hospital voluntarily, only to go downhill again. It takes courage and determination and one just has to ... trust. It was usually possible for Mrs D to find the necessary strength to continue cheerfully with the programme, for she is a courageous person and the inner resources which the illness revealed were remarkable. As she once said, 'It's growing-up time,' a realisation I had experienced once or twice when one

174

stops feeling sorry for oneself and accepts that no one ever promised that life would be easy, or comfortable, or straightforward.

I can only recall one occasion when Mrs D seriously faltered, and it was the direct result of a fanatical friend who 'kindly' wrote a very, very long letter.

It was a curious letter beginning, 'I was appalled to hear that you were on chemotherapy...' and we both reacted to it in the same way, assuming that it was a commiseration based on the discovery that Mrs D had cancer. But it wasn't. It continued: 'You should know that all of my friends who have gone the route of alternative therapies have survived and that those who have gone the route of conventional chemotherapy have not ...' and it continued like that for two long pages; attached to it was a great deal of whacky information about having one's bowels washed out, crystal treatments and ... Wellington boots with magnets in the soles. Her letter was a straightforward condemnation of the chemotherapy process, explaining how it was all unnecessary and that all one needed to do was to eat enough nut cutlets and all would be well.

My immediate reaction was to slip my colonic irrigator in my briefcase and go to visit the lady concerned, where I would have connected one end to the nearest fire hydrant and inserted the other in ... but I didn't. I wrote to her instead and pointed out the obvious, which was that she was the most insensitive, wooden-headed, crass person we had ever had the misfortune to meet. The best thing she could have done with her leaflets was to (and I quote my children here) ... 'shove them unceremoniously up her bottom'.

Not surprisingly, we have not heard from her since and, frankly, that is the way I would like our relationship to remain.

As Mrs D's treatments drew to a close and I found myself occasionally able once again to pull weeds in the garden, or walk the dog (provided he was tired out first), our thoughts turned to a good holiday. Nearly everyone we knew had, at some stage, said, 'I hope you're going to take a good holiday after all of this,' so we began to plan.

Years before we had, half in jest, remarked on an advert for the Venice-Simplon Orient Express and daydreamed of travelling to Venice on the train of trains, of satiating ourselves in works of art and architectural beauty, not to mention canals, and Mrs D resurrected the idea. We rattled the piggy-bank and decided to go. The decision was based not only on the idea that we would, without doubt, benefit from a good break, but also on the notion that we were, from now on, going to concentrate on the things we most wanted to do with our lives. Our ideals were not necessarily all as selfishly indulgent as riding to Italy on the world's plushest train, in fact quite the opposite, for we had, throughout our long periods of enforced incapacity, given a great deal of thought to 'what really matters', however clichéd a notion that might be. It is certainly not a revolutionary idea, for many who have reached a major life-crisis of some sort will, afterwards, often reflect on how it caused them to focus afresh, re-evaluate priorities and to change the emphasis of one's life.

It was not only Venice which beckoned, but also the simple pleasures of *Hercules*, for example. Many times we visualised it riding on the mooring in an exceptionally leafy corner of Leicestershire, where early morning sunshine glitters on the water and kingfishers dart in iridescent streaks of blue.

Not surprisingly, we had both been profoundly affected by all that had happened to us. It was as though the journey we had travelled together had caused us involuntarily to conclude that we wished to make the very most of those aspects of our lives we had previously valued, in a renewed effort to *treasure* them. Life became precious, not that it wasn't so before, but we had been given a new realisation that we cannot ever know what is just around the corner, or what the future will hold, and it caused us to redouble our efforts to be together doing the things which really matter.

I looked up from my desk and, through the window, noticed the dog bounding down the garden, tossing something small and white before him in his mouth. I couldn't see what it was; it certainly didn't have the mass of a ball, more that of a rolled sock. He was shaking it vigorously in mock battle. I thought nothing more of it until a little later.

Mrs Dudgeon came in with a puzzled expression on her face.

'Duncan, I must be getting forgetful. Do you think it's the chemotherapy? I washed my spare prosthesis, and I'm sure I hung it to dry beside the radiator, and now it has gone. I'm certain I put it there. Where else would I have put it?'

I suggested one or two alternative drying places, and as I did so my gaze turned towards the french windows where Fido stood, tail wagging, as if to say, 'Come out to play with me.'

And hanging from his teeth was a small, white bundle...

EPILOGUE

It has been quite a year. Believe it or not, as I sit writing this, the dog is beside me 'on crutches', having failed to clear a ditch in the woods and, two operations later, seems to have a kneecap which now faces the right way again. What else can go wrong, we wonder?

Mrs D finished her chemotherapy, which extended itself for an extra month because her immune system was rendered too vulnerable to maintain the treatments at their planned intervals. That seems to be fairly normal, particularly in the last couple of months of chemo. It wasn't a picnic but it was all bearable, and her prognosis is now very good. There will, of course, be continuous monitoring of her health which, as we have often commented, probably makes her safer than the average person in the street, who may be less rigorous about checking his or herself.

We persuaded Mrs Dudgeon that there was no truth in the rumour that she might benefit her white cell count by drinking white wine in the same way as she had boosted her red cells with red wine. She was very disappointed. Our diets have now undergone the most rigorous scrutiny as we have made the effort to research which foods promote the body's healthy responses for fighting cancer. We seem to consume huge amounts of vegetables, fruits, fish and pulses, and, where possible, we try to buy organic foods which, although more expensive, are, without doubt, much purer, having fewer man-made contaminants within them. Most important of all, we are enjoying life with each other.

My new hip is a total success. I haven't yet been through an airport scanner with it; that *is* something to look forward to. As for Seamus, his operation was such a success that he cycled several hundred miles for charity! My back is much better than it was, but I don't think it will ever be as strong as it used to be. You cannot thrash your body as I did and not have any consequences of such folly. Blame the Wally Factor.

I am often asked what I have discovered through our experiences. Without doubt, the life-lesson I have learned is about finding strength in apparently catastrophic adversity. I know it's a hackneyed old cliché, but you see, we really have had one of those years. Somehow one copes. *Somehow* one actually grows despite, or more likely *because* of it all. Yes, it has tested us to the boundaries of our endurance, but each time we reached those limits, they were mysteriously moved and replaced with more scope, more energy and more emotional resources to cope. It sounds trite to say we are richer for it all but, as I look at my manuscript, I am very aware that it is about far more than words, or fundraising for worthy cancer charities. As they say ... I guess you had to be there.

USEFUL ADDRESSES

CancerBACUP – helping people live with cancer

CancerBACUP is Europe's foremost provider of information and support to people affected by cancer. Its specialist nurses answer more than 50,000 enquiries a year – by phone, letter and at drop-in centres around the country. People affected by cancer – be they patients, relatives, friends or carers – can speak to a CancerBACUP specialist information nurse on FREEPHONE 0808 800 1234.

More than 50 booklets and 95 factsheets cover all aspects of cancer, cancer treatments and living with cancer. All the information is researched and written by experts in the field, and 200 specialists, in all areas of cancer, provide their expertise freely to ensure that the information is accurate and up to date. Just as importantly, information nurses and patients ensure that the information is clear and sensitively expressed. All CancerBACUP's publications are available on CD-ROM and on its website, www.cancerbacup.org.uk.

All CancerBACUP's services are funded by voluntary contributions.

Macmillan Cancer Relief

In the UK four in ten people will be diagnosed with cancer during their lifetime.

Driven by their needs Macmillan Cancer Relief is working towards the day when everyone in the UK has equal and ready access to the best information, treatment and care for cancer.

To achieve this goal, the charity funds services which include Macmillan nurses and doctors, and patient information and grants. It also builds Macmillan centres to provide information, support, treatment and care. These vital services help to achieve a better quality of life for people affected by cancer.

Macmillan works in partnership with the NHS. All of our services are free, and are funded entirely through the generosity of our supporters.

For more information, please contact:
Macmillan Cancer Relief
UK Office
89 Albert Embankment
London SE1 7UQ
Tel: 020 7840 7840
Fax: 020 7840 7841
Information line: 0845 601 6161
Website: www.macmillan.org.uk

BackCare

BackCare helps people manage back pain and prevent back injury by providing advice, promoting self-help, encouraging debate and funding scientific research into better back care

They have a telephone helpline and a network of self-help groups to support people with chronic back pain. They also publish a range of training and information materials, which are available from their offices. For further information, details of membership, or to order publications, please contact:

BackCare
16 Elmtree Road
Teddington
Middlesex TW11 8ST
Tel: 020 8977 5474
Fax: 020 8943 5183
Website: www.backpain.org
Email: back_pain@compuserve.com